CLEVELAND'S TREASURES
FROM THE
WORLD OF
BOTANICAL LITERATURE
by STANLEY H. JOHNSTON, JR.

CLEVELAND'S TREASURES FROM THE WORLD OF BOTANICAL LITERATURE

by STANLEY H. JOHNSTON, JR.

ORANGE FRAZER PRESS
Wilmington, Ohio USA

1998

ISBN: 1-882203-51-8
Copyright© 1998
by Stanley H. Johnston, Jr.
All rights reserved

Cover Design by Brooke Wenstrup

Additional copies of *Cleveland's Treasures from the World of Botanical Literature* or other Orange Frazer Press publications may be ordered directly from:

Orange Frazer Press, Inc.
Box 214
37 ¹/₂ West Main Street
Wilmington, Ohio 45177

Telephone 1.800.852.9332 for price and shipping information
Web Site: www.orangefrazer.com; E-mail address: editor@orangefrazer.com

Printed in Hong Kong

Library of Congress Cataloging-in-Publication Data
Johnston, Stanley H.
    Cleveland's treasures from the world of botanical literature / by
  Stanley H. Johnston, Jr.
        p.   cm.
    Includes bibliographical references (p.125).
    ISBN 1-882203-51-8
    1. Botanical literature--Ohio--Cleveland. 2. Botany--Pre-Linnean
works--Bibliography. 3. Botany--History. I. Holden Arboretum.
II. Cleveland Medical Library Association. III. Cleveland Botanical
Garden. IV. Title.
QK14.5J64   1998
580--dc21
                                                    98-21683
                                                      CIP

This book is dedicated to my wife, Carol, who has had to endure my years of researching and writing it; to Patsy Gerstner who has overseen the Cleveland Herbals Project from its inception to its completion; to Glen Jenkins and Ingrid Ebner who helped immeasurably with the research and proofing of the original drafts; to Mike Sands who has waited patiently to see his magnificent photographs of the works published; to the numerous donors, both individuals and foundations, whose generosity over the years has made the publications of this volume and the bibliographical volume possible; and above all to the collectors and donors of the books and artwork, without whom the treasures shown and discussed in the present book would not be available to enrich the lives of the Greater Cleveland community and attract scholars from around the world.

—Stanley H. Johnston

Acknowledgements

The generous support of the following made this work possible:

The American Foundation	Mr. James H. Marshall
Mrs. Benjamin P. Bole, Jr.	Mr. Richard H. Marshall
Mr. and Mrs. Clark E. Bruner	Mrs. William McDaniel Marshall
Mr. and Mrs. Robert R. Cull	Mr. William McDaniel Marshall, Jr.
Dr. and Mrs. Webb C. Chamberlain	Mr. T. W. Mastin
Mr. Harold Douthit	Ms. Genevieve Miller
Mrs. Allen H. Ford	The Norweb Foundation
Mr. Hugh Gibson	Mr. and Mrs. C. W. Eliot Paine
Mr. and Mrs. J. G. Havighurst	Mr. and Mrs. Hugh D. Pallister
Mr. and Mrs. Thomas Jenkins	Mr. and Mrs. Nicholas Peay
Mrs. Stanley Johnston	Mrs. James J. Rorimer
Mr. and Mrs. Theodore T. Jones	The Sherwick Fund
Mrs. Andrew A. Jyurovat	The S. K. Wellman Foundation
Mr. and Mrs. G. Robert Klein	Mr. and Mrs. A. W. Whitehouse

The Cleveland Botanical Garden, the Cleveland Medical Library Association, and the Holden Arboretum acknowledge this support with deep gratitude and appreciation.

Special thanks are also extended to the committee that took on the responsibility of funding this volume: Mrs. William McDaniel Marshall, chair, Mrs. Webb C. Chamberlain, Mrs. R. Henry Norweb, and C. W. Eliot Paine. Their advice and support in other matters of preparation and publication were invaluable, as were those of Brian E. Holley, Executive Director, and Joanna Bristol, Director of Information Services, The Cleveland Botanical Garden, and Richard H. Munson, Executive Director, The Holden Arobretum.

The exceptionally fine work of Michael W. Sands of Case Western Reserve University who photographed the illustrations reproduced in this book is gratefully acknowledged and will be appreciated by all who see this volume. The assistance of Glen Jenkins and Ingrid Ebner in the preparation of this work was invaluable. Finally, the efforts of Patsy Gerstner, who served as coordinator and administrator for this volume is acknowledged with sincere thanks.

Table of Contents

Introduction

IN 1992, THE HOLDEN Arboretum, the Cleveland Medical Library Association, and the Cleveland Botanical Garden (formerly the Garden Center of Greater Cleveland) joined together to publish *The Cleveland Herbal, Botanical, and Horticultural Collections*, a descriptive bibliographic study of pre-1830 books in their collections. Together, the collections in these three institutions represent one of the finest resources of its kind in the nation, and the books contain some of the most beautiful illustrations to be found in early printed books. In this book, Dr. Stanley H. Johnston painstakingly analyzed and described the structure of over 1000 titles and provided accompanying brief sketches of authors and illustrators. Because *The Cleveland Herbal, Botanical, and Horticultural Collections* is a complex book with highly specialized information, it was decided that a book for more general reading was in order. The result is this volume.

Books dealing with botanical literature generally fall into one of two categories: they are either authoritative scholarly studies (as is the 1992 volume) or they are books of exquisite illustrations. The latter seldom include much scholarly detail. This book, however, is different. It brings together both a sense of the scholarly and the enjoyment of the beauty.

This is, in fact, a book that can be enjoyed on many levels. It provides an introduction to some of the rarest, most interesting, and most significant botanical books published before 1830, giving the reader a taste of the kind of scholarly information available about these books, their authors and illustrators. It tells an intriguing story of the community of early botanists, allied by their interests, their conflicts, and their books. It can, of course, simply be enjoyed for its 140 glorious illustrations.

More than any of the above, even a cursory examination of the text and illustrations leaves the reader with a sense of the enormous scope, importance, and beauty of the collections that are in the Cleveland area. Cleveland has, without question, great treasures from the world of botanical literature.

A few notes for the reader

*U*NLESS NOTED OTHERWISE, books mentioned in the text are in one of the three Cleveland collections. If the specific location is not mentioned in the text, refer to the bibliography at the end of the work where the location is identified.

The location of books from which illustrations are used are identified in illustration captions as follows: CMLA – Allen Memorial Medical Library of the Cleveland Medical Library Association; GC – the Eleanor Squire Library of the Cleveland Botanical Garden; HA – the Warren H. Corning Library of the Holden Arboretum.

This book is a narrative and subject oriented treatment of many of the most important books described in detail in *The Cleveland Herbal, Botanical, and Horticultural Collections. A Descriptive Bibliography of Pre-1830 Works from the Libraries of the Holden Arboretum, the Cleveland Medical Library Association, and the Garden Center of*

Greater Cleveland, compiled by Stanley H. Johnston, Jr. (Kent State University Press, 1992). The reader might wish to make reference to this work for more information.

The bibliography at the end of *Cleveland's Treasures* includes all the Cleveland books mentioned in the text. Each entry includes a reference number to the entry in *The Cleveland Herbal, Botanical, and Horticultural Collections*.

The bibliography also includes the page number(s) on which the book is mentioned in *Cleveland's Treasures*.

A few footnotes appear throughout the text. These refer to specific secondary sources mentioned in the text. A full list of all secondary sources used in the preparation of this work is appended to the *The Cleveland Herbal, Botanical and Horticultural Collections*.

The Collectors

E OWE THE RICHNESS AND VARIETY OF THE CLEVELAND collections to two distinct groups of collectors. One group, comprised largely of early Cleveland physicians, one of whom was also a naturalist and horticulturist, created working collections that served their particular professional needs. As time passed, many of their books on plant science, botanical and herbal medicines, pharmacy, and horticulture became rare and important ones. The most significant working libraries are those of Jared Potter Kirtland (1793-1877), physician and naturalist, and several generations of the Cushing family of physicians (spanning the decades from the arrival of Erastus Cushing in Cleveland in 1832 until the death of his great grandson Edward Harvey Cushing in 1969

The other group of collectors consisted of distinguished bibliophiles who acquired books noted for their rarity, beauty, or other bibliophilic distinction. The leading bibliophiles were George Gehring Marshall (1890-1946) and Warren H Corning (1902-1975), although there were strong bibliophilic interests among the Cushings as well.

Collections associated with Kirtland and the Cushing family, and the George Gehring Marshall Collection are at the Cleveland Medical Library Association. The Warren H. Corning Collection is at the Holden Arboretum and the Cleveland Botanical Garden.

Jared Potter Kirtland was one of the four founders of the Cleveland Medical College (1843), the forerunner of today's School of Medicine at Case Western Reserve University. Kirtland was as well known as a naturalist and horticulturist as a physician. Both his medical and natural history libraries, used in the daily pursuit of his work and interests, are extensive. His books were given to Western Reserve University by his granddaughter, Mrs. Caroline P. Cutter, in 1900.

Kirtland was born in Wallingford, Connecticut, and under the tutelage of his grandfather had an extensive education in natural history while still a young man. Upon his grandfather's death, he inherited both the latter's library and

JARED POTTER KIRTLAND.

enough money to begin medical studies. He was the first student to matriculate at the Medical Institution of Yale College in 1813. While at Yale, he was a private student of Professor Eli Ives in botany and Professor Benjamin Silliman, Sr., in geology and mineralogy. The next year he went to the Medical Department of the University of Pennsylvania where he studied medicine under Benjamin Rush and botany under Benjamin Smith Barton. He returned to Yale and received his M.D. in 1815.

Kirtland practiced medicine in Connecticut where he also served for a period as a probate judge and local postmaster. After the loss of one of his two daughters in 1822 and his wife a year later, he moved to Poland, Ohio, where his father had served for many years as an agent for the Connecticut Land Company. In Ohio, Kirtland taught medicine at the Medical School of Cincinnati, the Willoughby Medical College, and the Cleveland Medical College. In Cleveland, he acquired a farm in what is now Lakewood. He devoted himself to the creation of a model farm and orchard where he could experiment with improved varieties of flowers and fruits.

The wealth of the Kirtland Collection is supplemented by several letterbooks in the archives of the Cleveland Medical Library Association covering the period from 1850-1856. They were originally deposited there as part of the effects of Dr. S. W. Kelley, a noted Cleveland physician. These letters touch virtually all aspects of his interests, including his horticultural efforts in crossbreeding and grafting cherries.

Erastus Cushing was the first of four generations of Cushings to practice medicine in Cleveland. His son, Henry Kirke Cushing, and his grandsons, Edward Fitch Cushing and Harvey Williams Cushing, were noted physicians, although Harvey Cushing's career was not in Cleveland. Rather, he was associated with Harvard and Yale. Because of his pioneering work in neurosurgery. Harvey Cushing is regarded as America's first neurosurgeon. Edward Harvey Cushing, the son of Edward Fitch, was intimately associated with the Cleveland Medical Library Association, serving on its board of trustees from 1932 to 1942, as Curator of Incunabula from 1929 to 1937, and as Director from 1938 to 1942.

Many of the Cushing books were assembled and used by various family members in connection with their medical practices. Strong bibliophilic interests account, however, for others. For example, the 1609 edition of Sir Kenelm Digby's *Of Bodies and Of Man's Soul, Of the Powder of Sympathy, and Of the Vegetation of Plants* was given to Harvey Cushing by the noted bibliophile and physician, Sir William Osler, in 1909. Harvey Cushing, in turn, presented it to his nephew, Edward Harvey Cushing, who gave it to the Library Association..

The presence of a rare collection of late medieval and early renaissance volumes, predominantly medical in character, is due to Edward Harvey Cushing's strong bibliophilic interests. The collection formed part of the library of Nicolaus Pol (ca. 1470-1532), physician to Emperor Maximilian I and resident of Innsbruck in Austria. Pol had a fine library that was especially strong in theological and medical works. After his death, his library was housed in the Collegiate Church of San Candido at Innichen, near Innsbruck, where the greater part of it remains today. At some point, however, the medical books made their way to the marketplace and after changing hands a few times were offered for sale in 1929 by Maggs Brothers (dealers in rare volumes) in London. Cushing, who was at that time Curator of Incunabula for the Library Association, recognized their importance, and money for their purchase was secured from an anonymous donor who gave the collection as a memorial to Mr. Charles H. Bingham. In the years that followed, additional Pol volumes were acquired and added to the collection.

The jewel of the medical botanical collections belonging to the Cleveland Medical Library Association is the George Gehring Marshall Collection. Marshall was born in 1890, the son of Wentworth G. and Louise Gehring Marshall. Wentworth Marshall was the founder of the Marshall Drug Company, a leading drug company in the city for many years. George spent his childhood on the family's Rocky Run Farm near Northfield, Ohio, in an area that is now part of the Cuyahoga Valley National Recreation Area. This experience and the encouragement of his father and his uncle, Dr. John George Gehring, directed his attention to botany and horticulture, the historical use of plants (and animals) in pharmacy, and book collecting.

Marshall graduated from Adelbert College of Western Reserve University in 1914 with honors in English. The following year, he received his Ph.C. from Western Reserve University's School of Pharmacy on completion of a thesis on *Animal Drugs Used in Medicine during the Middle Ages in England and France*. Following his graduation, he entered the family business, of which he eventually became vice-president and treasurer, and, on his father's death in 1936, president.

EDWARD HARVEY CUSHING.
Courtesy of the Cleveland Medical Library Association.

GEORGE GEHRING MARSHALL.
Courtesy of the Marshall Family.

early in his career, although his most active collecting years were from 1925 to 1930. His collection is especially strong in fifteenth, sixteenth, and seventeenth century herbals and illustrated floral works. Tulips were of special interest to him, a fact reflected by many of the titles in his collection of nearly 300 works. Flower books that show the development of the engraver's art in the 17th century are another important part of the collection. However, it has been recognized that the most valuable part of the collection is a group of about 80 herbals, that is, books that deal with the medicinal use of plants.

After Marshall's death in 1946, the Cleveland Medical Library Association purchased the collection from his widow, Louise McDaniel Marshall, through the agency of Cleveland book dealer, Peter Keisogloff.

As the Marshall Collection is one jewel among the Cleveland treasures, the Warren H. Corning Collection of Horticultural Classics at the Holden Arobretum and the Cleveland Botanical Garden is another.

Warren Holmes Corning was a third generation Clevelander. He was born in 1902, the son of Henry Wick and Edith W. Corning. The family resided in Bratenahl. Warren graduated from Harvard University in 1924 and entered the banking and investment business, later becoming president of Corning and Company, an investment advisory firm. In the early 1930's, he and his wife, Maud Eells Corning, purchased land for a home in Lake County, which they called Lantern Court. The house and gardens are now maintained by the Holden Arboretum.

Corning's involvement with the Holden Arboretum dates to the 1930's when it was administered from the Cleveland Museum of Natural History. Appointed to the Holden Ar-

His interest in botany and book collecting was a life-long pursuit. He collected plants, conducted botanical experiments, developed an arboretum at the Rocky Run Farm, served in later years as a trustee of the Dawes Arboretum in Newark, Ohio, and contributed trees for the landscaping of the Crile General Hospital, which was opened in 1944 to treat World War II veterans. At the time of his death, he was engaged in a project to restore the white pine forests of Ohio.

Marshall began collecting herbals, garden and flower books, medical recipe books, pharmacopoeias, dispensatories, and so forth

boretum Board of the Cleveland Museum of Natural History in 1937, he was subsequently given oversight of the oriental ornamental plantings there. He served as the first unpaid executive administrator (director) of the Holden Arboretum until 1959 and served on its board of trustees for many years and on its advisory committee. His deep interest in the Arboretum and his foresight led him to encourage the Arboretum in land acquisition and to give land himself for its purposes.

His association with the Cleveland Botanical Garden dates from about the same time and developed from his avid interest in gardening and flowers.

Corning's interest in collecting rare botanical volumes was an outgrowth of his interest in art, as well as in flowers and gardening. The beauty and artistic skill of the illustrations in these books were of enduring interest to him, and this interest is clearly apparent in his collection. He began recording his book collecting in a series of small black notebooks with books purchased in 1940. These records, along with his correspondence with dealers, invoices, and annotated dealers' catalogues, all of which are at the Holden Arboretum, attest to his deep commitment to assembling an exceptionally fine collection.

Corning's collection is far larger in scope than any of the other Cleveland collections and contains some of the rarest works in the field, including the only known copy of one prospectus, numerous works of which only five to one hundred copies are known, and several works containing extra plates beyond those normally found. A collection of unusually rich provenance, it includes books that once graced the Boissier-Candole Library (the combined libraries of these two great botanists) and ones owned by Charles Darwin (evolutionary biologist), Aylmer Bourke Lambert (amateur botanist and patron), Sir James Edward Smith (British physician and botanist), and others. It also contains a small collection of original manuscripts, including a rare Humphry Repton "red book," and several thousand original botanical paintings, including works by artists as diverse as Claude Aubriet, Georg Dionysius Ehret, Pierre Joseph Redouté, Jean Christoph Heyland,

WARREN HOLMES CORNING.
Reprinted with permission from *The Plain Dealer* @1971.
All Rights Reserved.

Pancrace Bessa, Tecophile Colla, and Mitsunari Tosa, among others.

Cleveland is fortunate to have had these several people who, for different reasons, assembled collections of books that enhance our understanding of the past by preserving information and by making it possible for each of us to enjoy the beauty that accompanied the written word. Without such collectors, the people of Cleveland would not have access to this remarkable treasurehouse of botanical and horticultural art and knowledge. These collections provide a resouce for study and enjoyment today that has few parallels.

CHAPTER I

Herbal and Medical Botanical Works

CCORDING TO THE OXFORD ENGLISH DICTIONARY, an herbal is "a book containing the names and descriptions of herbs, or plants in general, with their properties and virtues." The same source defines an herb as "a plant of which the stem does not become woody and persistent, but remains more or less soft and succulent, and dies down to the ground (or entirely) after flowering." Further, the term is also "applied to plants, of which the leaves, or stems and leaves, are used for food or medicine, or in some way for their scent or flavour."

According to these definitions, the key elements of an herbal are the name of the plant, its physical description, and its properties and virtues. Names often appear in the form of a synonymy giving all the different names which the current writer thinks have been applied to the same plant. The physical description is usually accompanied by an illustration, and in later works the description is expanded to sometimes include locations where the plant is most likely to be found and details of its life cycle and/or cultivation. The list of the plant's properties and virtues, sometimes include detailed instructions for its medicinal use. For the purposes of our discussion, the term herbal will be used only when all three of these key elements are present in at least a most rudimentary form.

The Cleveland collections are fortunate to possess a copy of the 1483 second issue of the earliest fully illustrated printed herbal, the ***Herbarium*** of Apuleius, which was printed at Rome by Joannes Philippus de Lignamine, a Sicilian courtier to Pope Sixtus IV in 1481. It is of particular interest for its extremely crude or highly stylized (depending on one's point of view) depictions of plants accompanied by

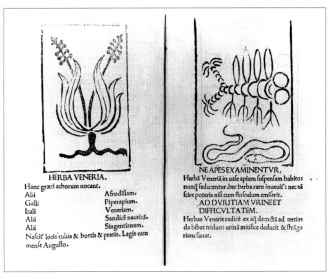

HERBA VENEREA, woodcut. Apuleius,
Herbarium, 1483. (HA).

ALKENGE. Hand-colored woodcut. *Herbarius Latinus,* 1484. (CMLA).

images of animals whose bites or stings they were believed to heal. The pictures are important because they are thought to represent a school of botanical draughtsmanhip derived from late Roman art, and their texture has suggested that they may also be the earliest metal cuts of plants.

In 1484, Peter Schoeffer printed the first edition of the *Herbarius Latinus*. It was the second illustrated herbal, one of the earliest works to have a title page, and the first herbal printed in Germany. Schoeffer started as a calligrapher, became foreman in Gutenberg's shop, and began printing in collaboration with Johann Fust as early as 1457. The *Herbarius Latinus* was the first printed herbal to attract a wide readership as evidenced by the fact that it was published in 11 editions before 1500, with the last edition published in 1565. Cleveland has two copies of the first edition, as well as copies of the Passau editions of 1485 and 1486-1487, the Vicenza edition of 1491, the Venice editions of 1499 and 1509, and an edition of the *Herbolario Volgare*, the Italian translation of the work, published in 1536.

A book of somewhat wider scope in the Cleveland collections is the *Hortus Sanitatis* first published in 1491 by Jacob Meydenbach at Mainz. Medieval in nature, with a mixture of real and mythical plants, animals, birds, fishes, and minerals, the work is a combination of a natural history and a guide to medicinal materials. It is highlighted by a series of interesting woodcuts illustrating most of the chapters. The second edition, published by Jacob Prüss at Strassburg in 1497, reduced the size of the book from 454 to 360 leaves by the use of more lines per column and a smaller type and became the model on which all subsequent editions were based.

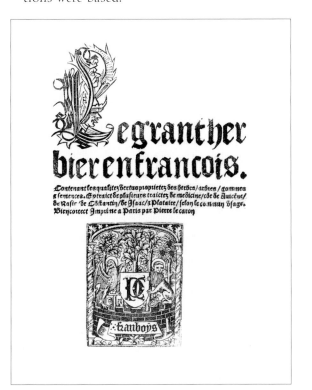

TITLE PAGE. *Le Grant Herbier,* circa 1499. (CMLA).

One of the rarer early herbals in the collections is **Le Grant Herbier** published in Paris circa 1499 by Pierre Le Caron. This compilation includes the text of the **Circa Instans** an antidotarium (or book of antidotes) believed written by Matthaeus Platearius the younger (fl. circa 1150), who was one of the teachers of the School of Salerno. It was first published circa 1486-1488 under the title of **Arbolayre**. The English translation, however, takes its introduction and conclusion from the **German Herbarius** and the **Hortus Sanitatis**, and was first published by Peter Treveris in 1526 as **The Grete Herball**. It bears the distinction of being the second herbal published in English and the first illustrated English herbal.

The first herbal published in English was printed by Richard Bancke in 1525 and has been popularly dubbed **Banckes' Herbal**. Unfortunately there are no copies in the Cleveland collections of this landmark in English printing which is believed to have been based on a lost medieval manuscript.

Somewhat different in nature is the **De Viribus Herbarum** usually ascribed to Macer Floridus, but generally believed to have been written by Odo of Meung. The work is a poem in Latin hexameters describing the medicinal powers of from 77 to 97 herbs (depending on the edition and the manuscript upon which it was based). The Cleveland copies are relatively late editions, having been printed circa 1515 and in 1530, while the first printed edition appeared in 1477. The 1530 edition, bearing the title **De Herbarum Virtutibus**, is of interest in that it contains an expanded commentary on the poem by Johannus Atrocianus, a professor of mathematics in Basel, and is accompanied by an edition of Walahfrid Strabo's **Hortulus**, a

WOODCUT. *Hortus Sanitatis,* 1491. (CMLA).

poem on the herbs and garden of the abbey of Reichenau in Baden, Germany, that was originally written in the ninth century A.D.

Other medicinal works in the collections which were cast in the forms of poems, chiefly as mnemonic aids to students or would be practitioners, include the *Theriaca* and *Alexipharmaca* of Nicander of Colophon, and the *Regimen Sanitatis* of the School of Salerno. The poems by Nicander, which were composed in the second century B.C., deal respectively with the bites of poisonous animals and their antidotes and vegetable poisons and their antidotes. The editions in Cleveland include the first separate edition printed in the original Greek by Aldus Manutius and Andreas Asulani in 1522-1523; the first French translation published in 1567, which was done in poetic form by Jacques Grevin, the French physician better known as a poet and playwright; the Latin translation of Euricius Cordus published in 1571; and the first three text edition featuring the Greek original, the Latin translation of Jean de Gorris, and the Italian translation of A. M. Salvini, which was published in 1764.

The *Regimen Sanitatis* is a Latin poem supposed to have been composed circa 1100 A.D. by an author or authors associated with the School of Salerno, one of the earliest medical schools of the Christian West. In its original form, the work was a lengthy poem consisting of advice on how to preserve health, rules of diet and hygiene, simple therapeutics, and other general instructions of a practical nature. Owing to its manuscript history, the length and contents of the printed versions may vary considerably. The Cleveland collections include the 1541 fourth edition of the first English translation, two Latin editions of 1622 and 1638 under the title *Medicina Salernitana*, and a Latin version published in 1649 titled *Schola Salernitana*.

The sixteenth century saw the appearance of a number of major figures in Germany, three

of whom, Otto Brunfels, Hieronymus Bock, and Leonhart Fuchs, have come to be known as the "German Fathers of Botany."

Otto Brunfels began his career as a Carthusian monk but decided against this calling. Having committed himself to a monastic life, it was literally necessary for him to engineer an escape from the monastery, after which he became an itinerant Protestant preacher and the author of a large number of theological tracts. He later started a school for boys at Strassburg and subsequently obtained his medical degree at Basel and was appointed town physician to Berne in 1533.

Brunfels' *Herbarum Vivae Eicones* was first published in three volumes issued in 1530, 1532, and 1536. The plants represented are generally medicinal in nature and the text is marked by numerous learned references to medieval, Arabic, and classical sources. The second volume is of particular interest in that, among a series of 12 essays on plants or errors in earlier authors, are articles by both Bock and Fuchs. The main importance of the work, however, lies in the highly realistic treatment of the plants in the woodcuts which were based on the designs from live models done by Hans Weiditz.

The second, and probably most important, of the "German Fathers of Botany" is Hieronymus Bock, who was also known as Hieronymus Tragus and Hieronymus Herbarius. Although Bock's parents intended that he should enter the monastic life, he attended a university (where he may have studied medicine) and became a schoolteacher before becoming superintendent of the gardens of the Count Palatine Ludwig. Owing to the exigencies of the Reformation, his later years were spent in an on-again off-again career as a Lutheran minister.

Urged by Brunfels and others, Bock undertook to prepare an herbal for the German people. It first appeared in 1539 as the

Helleborus Niger.

Chriſtwurtz.

DE VTROQVE HELLEBORO,
ALBO, ET NIGRO,
Rhapſodia   Secunda.
❧ Nomenclaturæ Albi.

Græcæ,   ἑλλέβορ☉. λινκόσ. ἀσκίσ. πιγνατόξιρισ. γόνοσ ὑράκλιοσ.
πολύιιλοσ. ἀνάφυς☉.

Latinæ,   Helleborus albus.   Veratrum album.
Teutonicç,   Weiß Nyeßwurtz.

❧ Nomenclaturæ Nigri

Græcæ,   ἑλλέβοροσ μέλασ. μιλαμπόδιον. πολύρριζον. μιλανόρριζον.

Latinæ,   Helleborus niger.   Prætion.   Veratrum nigrum.
Teutonicæ,   Chriſtwurtz.

HELLEBORUS NIGER, woodcut by Hans Weiditz. Otto Brunfels,
Herbarum Vivae Eiconest, 1531-1536. (CMLA).

New Kreütter Büch von
vnderscheydt/würckung vnd namen der kreüt
ter so in Teütschen landē wachsen. Auch der selbigen eygent=
lichem vnd wolgegründtem gebrauch in der Artznei/zü behal=
ten vnd zü fürdern leibsgesuntheyt fast nutz vnd tröst=
lichen / vorab gemeynem verstand. Wie das
auß dreien Registern hienach ver=
zeychnet ordenlich züfinden.

Beschriben durch Hieronymum Bock auß lang=
wiriger vnnd gewisser erfarung / vnnd gedruckt zü
Straßburg / durch Wendel Rihel. Jm jar
M. D XXXIX.

Wie Keyserlicher freiheyt auff vij . vnd
Königlicher auff vj.jar.

New Kreütter Buch. It differed considerably from the previous work of Brunfels and the later work of Fuchs in that it was a local flora covering all German plants and not confined only to those believed to have medicinal properties. As such, it was intended as an aid to the identification

of plants for the German people and was written originally in the vernacular, whereas the works of Brunfels and Fuchs, intended for a more international audience, were originally written in Latin. The real importance of the work, however, lies in the study which Bock devoted to each plant as evidenced in the methodical and detailed descriptions which are the prototype of modern phytography (or plant description). Such descriptions were necessary since the first edition was unillustrated. Beginning with the second edition of 1546, entitled *Kreuter Buch*, the herbal was embellished by the decorative woodcuts of David Kandel, many of which were modeled on the earlier illustrations in the works of Brunfels and Fuchs and many of which are expanded through the addition of genre scenes illustrative of popular stories regarding specific plants. The work was finally translated into Latin by the unfortunate David Cyber, who died of the plague at the age of 28, a year after completing the translation. It was published in 1552.

The third of the "German Fathers of Botany" was Leonhart Fuchs. Fuchs was a physician who was twice professor of medicine at the University of Ingolstadt, served five years as court physician to the Margrave Georg von Brandenburg, and spent the last 31 years of his life as professor of medicine at the Protestant University of Tübingen. Prior to the publication of his herbal, Fuchs had acquired an international reputation for his cure of the sweating sickness, an epidemic and deadly disease, probably caused by a virus.

In the ***De Historia Stirpium***, first published in 1542, Fuchs sought to provide his readers with the classical descriptions of Dioscorides, Pliny, and other authors from antiquity, supported for purposes of identification by large illustrations of what he took to be the same plants. Indeed, the work is generally best known for the large accurate, but idealized, illustrations which were drawn from nature by Albrecht Meyer, transferred to woodblocks by Heinrich Füllmaurer, and cut into wood by Veit Rudolf Speckle, all of whom are immortalized along with Fuchs through woodcut portraits in the book. His work's other chief claims to fame are the presence of the first attempt at a list of botanical nomenclature and the first illustration of maize which Fuchs mistakenly described as coming from Turkey.

Although not one of the traditional "Fathers," mention should be made at this point of Jacobus Theodorus, better known as Tabernaemontanus, who is also represented in the Cleveland collections. Another Protestant German physician, Theodorus had been a pupil of both Brunfels and Bock. He labored 36 years on his herbal, which appeared under the title ***Neuw Kreuterbuch*** in 1587 and 1591.

Deserving credit as a fourth "German Father of Botany" is Valerius Cordus. Although dismissed by the German botanical historians of the nineteenth century, his fame among the botanists of the sixteenth and seventeenth century has been restored through the research of Edward L. Greene.[1] Valerius was the son of the celebrated physician, philologist, academic, and botanist, Euricius Cordus, who gave him his early training in botany. Valerius learned about medicinal plants while working in his uncle's pharmacy shop. On a more formal level, he obtained a bachelor's degree from the University

of Marburg and studied at the University of Wittenberg, where he also delivered a series of lectures on Dioscorides. Wishing to see the plants described by the ancients, Valerius departed for Italy in 1542, where he visited the Universities of Padua, Ferrara, and Bologna before setting out for Rome with several companions in 1544. There he died suddenly, at the age of twenty-nine, apparently the victim of both malaria and a kick from a horse.

Although Cordus wrote extensively, all of his works are currently believed to have been published posthumously. The earliest of his published works was the ***Dispensatorium***, a work on preparing all medicines. It was originally written while he worked in the pharmacy of Joachim Ralla, his uncle, and now believed to have been published for the first time in 1546. This work, which became the first official pharmacopoeia of the city of Nuremberg, is represented in the Cleveland collections by a relatively late edition published in 1608.

The bulk of Cordus's botanical material did not appear, however, until 1561, when it was published with some other material in a volume under the editorship of Conrad Gesner. Among the material here printed for the first time are the ***Annotationes in Pedacii Dioscoridis*** based on notes taken from Cordus's lectures at Wittenberg, and the first four books of Cordus's herbal, the ***Historiae Stirpium***. A companion volume published in 1563 included the fifth and final book of the ***Historiae Stirpium*** that was based on the material that Cordus had written on the plants of Italy in the course of his fatal trip. It also contains accounts of his death.

The importance of Cordus's herbal to botany lies in the scientific and detailed examinations and descriptions of plants based on live mature specimens. These incorporate descriptions of all parts and include detailed accounts of the flowers and fruit where appropriate, records of odors and flavors of foliage,

[1]Green, Edward L., *Landmarks of Botanical History*. Edited by Frank N. Edgerton, with contributions by Robert P. McIntosh and Rogers McVaugh. 2 vol. A publication of the Hunt Institute for Botanical Documentation, Carnegie-Mellon University. Stanford, Calif.: Stanford University Press, 1983.

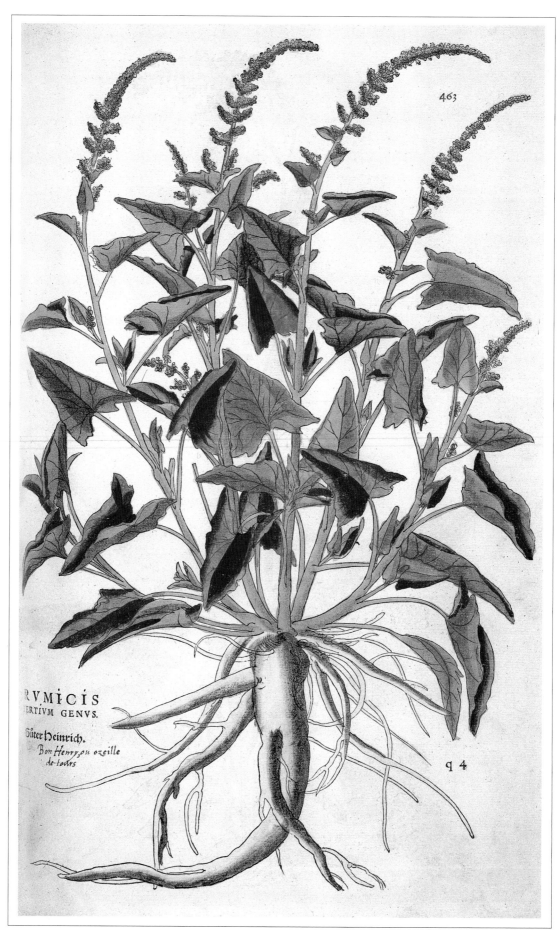

RVMICIS.
ERTIVM GENVS.

Güter Heinrich.
Bon Henry, ou ozeille
de tours

463

q 4

RUMICIS. Woodcut by Veit Rudolf Speckle and Heinrich Füllmaurer after
Albrecht Meyer, hand-colored for the publisher. Leonhart Fuchs,
De Historia Stirpium Commentarii Insignes, 1542.(HA).

flowers, and roots, and a brief mention of any medicinal use. Indeed, Greene indicates, on the basis of these descriptions, that in his view Cordus rather than Bock should be regarded as laying the foundation for modern phytography, since he wrote in Latin for a learned international audience while Bock wrote in the vernacular for a more limited audience. Greene also notes that much confusion has been caused over the years by scholars noting discrepancies between Cordus's descriptions and the woodcuts which accompany them in the mistaken belief that Cordus intended the work to be illustrated. In fact the woodcuts, which were mainly from the stock cut for the illustrated versions of Bock's herbal, were inserted by Gesner at the insistence of the printer to make the work more marketable.

Prior to Cordus the main thrust of herbals was the representation of medicinal plants known to the ancients in a manner which would make them identifiable to the physician, pharmacist, student, or in some cases, layman of the time. The medicinal textbooks were essentially those which had been used throughout the medieval period and included authors such as Dioscorides, Serapion the younger, Aetius of Amida, Celsus, Avicenna, Albengnefit, Alkindus, Ibn Butlan, and Mesue all of whom had significant sections dealing with the use of botanical simples. These works, which are essentially the medicinal source books of the herbal authors, are particularly well represented in the Cleveland Medical Library Association collections.

The most important of these works to the authors of the early herbals was the work of Pedanius Dioscorides which is generally known under its Latin title of *De Materia Medica*. This seminal pharmacological work, which was not limited to botanical simples, but also included animal and mineralogical drugs, was originally written in Greek in Asia Minor sometime during the first century A.D. It was first published in a Latin edition of 1479. The Cleveland collections include five Latin editions published between 1516 and 1830, as well as German, French, and Italian translations.

De Materia Medica presented a number of problems to Renaissance scholars. One of them was the simple fact that over the centuries of manuscript copying, numerous scribal errors had crept into the text. An early response to this problem was the work of Ermolao Barbaro, a Venetian scholar and diplomat prior to his appointment to the Patriarchate of Aquileia. The 1516 edition of *De Materia Medica* features a Latin translation of the work by him, to which is appended a work entitled *Corollarium*. In it, Barbaro attempted to condense all that had been written by the Greek and Roman authors on the plants described by Dioscorides. He thus hoped to make the original information clearer in meaning.

T THE SAME TIME that scholars were dealing with scribal errors, physicians and scholars in Northern Europe and Italy were creating other problems by attempting to apply the descriptions of Dioscorides, (based on species indigenous mainly to Asia Minor) to their local flora. This resulted in frequent misidentifications and sometimes disastrous results. Even in the herbals of Brunfels and Fuchs, where the primary goal was to depict the plants of Dioscorides and the other medicinal writers with sufficient clarity that another plant could not be mistaken for it, there was a tendency to equate European species of similar features with the plants of Asia Minor described by Dioscorides. This problem was further complicated in a rare 1543 abridgement of Brunfels' herbal entitled *In Dioscoridis Historiam Herbarum Certissima*

Adaptio. It limited itself to portraying those plants described by Dioscorides with woodcuts from his *Herbarum Vivae Eicones* supplemented by a number of new cuts, which were also based on German specimens.

As the grip of the medieval concept of authority loosened, debate over the accuracy of text and the correctness of plant identification were main topics of the learned and medical communities. This is revealed in the 1528 and 1535 editions of Giovanni Manardo's *Epistolae Medicinales,* where book eight is primarily concerned with correspondence regarding the relative merits of the Latin translations of Dioscorides by Ermolao Barbaro and Marcello Virgilio.

The best known of the Renaissance commentators on Dioscorides was Pier Andrea Mattioli, an Italian doctor who served successively as physician to Archduke Ferdinand I and Emperor Maximilian II. Mattioli's edition of Dioscorides first appeared as a translation into Italian based on Jean Ruel's Latin edition with relatively few commentaries in 1544. The earliest edition of Dioscorides with Mattioli's commentaries in the Cleveland collections is the Latin version published at Lyons in 1554, at which point the annotations are still relatively brief. As time went on the annotations, which came to include information on all plants known to Mattioli, not just those known to Dioscorides, overwhelmed the text of Dioscorides (which is sometimes omitted entirely). The work is generally known under its Latin title, *Commentarii.*

Many other scholars continued to be concerned with Dioscorides. In 1536, Juan Rodriguez de Castello Branco, a Christianized Jew of Spanish extraction who was born in Portugal and wrote under the pseudonym of Amatus Lusitanus, published his initial commentaries on the first two books of Dioscorides. The first edition to cover all five books of Dioscorides appeared in 1553, with

the last and only illustrated edition appearing in 1558 under the title of *In Dioscoridis Anazarbei De Materia Medica Libros Quinque Enarrationes*. The work included a scholarly examination of the errors in the text of Mattioli accompanied by attacks on certain aspects of the works produced by Brunfels, Fuchs, Jean Ruel, and Mattioli. The criticism did not go

PISTACIA, large woodcut version. Pier Andrea Mattioli, *Commentarii in Sex Libros Pedaci Dioscoridis Anazarbei De Materia Medica,* 1583. (GC).

unnoticed by Mattioli who responded with a scathing attack on Amatus entitled *Apologia Adversus Amathum Lusitanum* that accompanied the 1558 Latin edition of the *Commentarii*. Amatus's notoriety, Mattioli's enmity, and the accession of Pope Paul IV, who actively persecuted the Christianized Jews, led to a series of forced flights for Amatus from regions of papal authority or influence. This finally led him to Salonica in Greece, where he died after contracting the plague from one of his patients.

Another student of Dioscorides who ran afoul of Mattioli was Luigi Anguillara. Anguillara was born as Luigi Squalermo, the son of Francesco Squalermo, physician to Pope Leo X. Also known as Aloysius Romanus, Anguillara took his medical degree at an early age from the University of Ferrara, worked with Luigi Ghini in Ghini's botanical garden in Bologna, and was appointed the first director of the botanical garden in Padua in 1546. Anguillara traveled extensively in his quest to determine the drugs used by the ancients, at the same time recording data on such new plants as he might find. He is also known to have medically tested at least one of the plants in treating himself and other patients for epilepsy. The results of Anguillara's work appeared in the form of a series of letters to various patrons which were published in 1561 as the *Semplici*. Although much admired by Conrad Gesner and others, the work contradicted some of the views of Mattioli. Fortunately for Anguillara, he was better able to withstand the public and private attacks of Mattioli than Amatus was because of his connections and relation with the establishment. Nonetheless, it is believed that the combined enmity of Mattioli and Ulisse Aldrovandi (zoologist and pupil of Gesner) forced Anguillara's resignation from his posts in Padua in the same year that his publication appeared.

Later commentaries on Dioscorides are included in the *Oeuvres* (1628) of Jacques and Paul Contant, who were father and son pharmacists of Poitiers. Also included in the book is a poetical account of the botanical and natural history collections assembled by Paul Contant during his travels on the continent, a more detailed poetical account of his medicinal botanical garden entitled *Le Second Eden*, and a prose analysis under the title *Synopsis Plantarum*.

LE SECOND EDEN, engraved title page by Pinson after Contant. Jacques and Paul Contant, *Les Oeuvres,* 1628. (HA).

TITLE PAGE of volume eight featuring a hand-colored
vignette of Mt. Athos engraved by R. Williamson.
John Sibthorp, James Edward Smith and John Lindley,
Flora Graeca, 1806-1840 (actually one of the later copies
issued by H. G. Bohn with original leaves of
text but later printings of the plates on paper
watermarked 1845). HA.

The search for the plants described by
Dioscorides continued through the eighteenth
century and culminated with the publication
of the *Florae Graecae Prodromus* (1806-1813
[-1816]) and the *Flora Graeca* (1806-1840).
These were the work of John Sibthorp, an
English physician and botanist, who succeeded
his father as Sherardian professor of botany
at Oxford.

In 1786, Sibthorp visited Vienna where he
consulted the great illustrated manuscript of
the writings of Dioscorides, the **Codex
Vindobonensis**, made the acquaintance of
Jacquin, and secured the services of the young
Ferdinand Bauer as an artist. During the following year, Sibthorp and Bauer botanized
through Greece, the islands, and Asia Minor,
before returning to Oxford, where Bauer worked
on his illustrations. In 1794-1795, Sibthorp
undertook a second expedition to the Levant
in the course of which he contracted an un-
specified disease which led to his death the
following year. Sibthorp left his estate to Oxford University with the provision that they
undertake to publish the results of his expedition along with the illustrations done by Bauer.
The task of completing the **Prodromus** and editing and providing botanical descriptions for
the plants in the **Flora Graeca** fell to James Edward Smith, the first president of the Linnean
Society of London, who had earlier outbid
Sibthorp for the Linnaean collections. Smith
lived to see the publication of the **Prodromus**
and to complete the first six and a half volumes of the **Flora Graeca**. The remaining three
and a half volumes were completed after his death
by John Lindley. The original edition proved
to be enormously expensive and was limited to
somewhere between 25 and 30 copies. Sometime between 1845 and 1847, H. G. Bohn issued a second issue of 40 additional copies
using the sheets of text from the original printing but with new printings of the plates on
paper watermarked between 1845 and 1847. One
such copy is at The Holden Arboretum.

The medicinal authorities used by the writers of the early herbals are particularly well represented in the collections of the Cleveland
Medical Library Association which are in the
Allen Memorial Medical Library.

The Pol Collection at the Allen Library consists of a series of books which were originally acquired by Nicolaus Pol (circa 1470-1532). Pol served as pharmacist to Duke Sigismund at Innsbruck, and after obtaining his medical doctorate in 1494, served as physician to the Emperors Maximilian I and Charles V. Although only a small part of Pol's total library, the Cleveland collection provides a representative grouping of the medical works used by Pol and his contemporaries.[2]

Pol is of special interest as a medicinal botanical writer because of his account of the guaiac cure for syphilis, which he investigated along with Paul Ricius and Hieronymus Carazolus on an expedition to Spain on behalf of Matthew Lang, Cardinal

MANUSCRIPT SIGNATURE of Nicolaus Pol from a volume in the Pol Collection. (**CMLA**).

of Gurk and Bishop Coadjutor of Salzburg. The report, entitled *De Cura Morbi Gallici Per Lignum Guaycanum Libellus*, is dated 19 December 1517 in the text, making it one of the earliest accounts of the treatment, although the printed version did not appear until 1535.

Ricius, who was one of the physicians who accompanied Pol on the expedition to Spain, adopted the guaiac treatment in his own practice. One of his patients was Ulrich von Hutten, a knight who was a friend of Martin Luther and the man who literally helped Brunfels escape from the monastery. Hutten was so impressed with the results of the treatment that he wrote a short treatise discussing the treat-

[2]A substantial account of Pol's medical library is given in Max Fisch, Nicolaus Pol Doctor 1494. New York: [Anthoensen Press, Portland, Me., for:] Herbert Reichner for the Cleveland Medical Library Association, 1947.

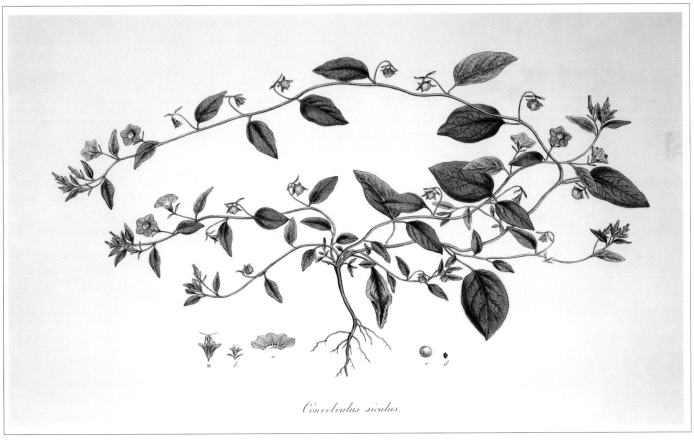

Convolvulus siculus.

CONVULVUS SICULUS by Ferdinand Bauer. John Sibthorp, James Edward Smith, and John Lindley, *Flora Graeca*, 1806-1840 (actually one of the later copies with original leaves of text but later printings of the plates on paper watermarked 1845). HA.

ment entitled *De Guaiaci Medicina et Morbo Gallico*. This work, which was published from Johann Schoeffer's shop in Mainz in 1519, is the second earliest printed account of the treatment, the first having been an anonymous account which appeared a few months prior to this publication. Unfortunately, guaiac was only a stimulant and sudorific and not a cure for syphilis, and Hutten died of the disease three years after the publication of his supposed cure.

Some 270 years later Francisco Xavier de Balmis introduced another botanical cure for syphilis into Spain. The treatment was an Indian medicine originally promoted by Nicolas Viana. In the course of experimenting with the treatment in the syphilis ward of the Hospital de San Andrés in Mexico, Balmis determined it was composed primarily of the ground roots of agave and begonia. Balmis was commissioned to introduce the treatment into Spain in 1792, but was denounced as a charlatan by a special commission which had been appointed to examine Balmis's work. Balmis responded by publishing a description of the treatment and case histories of its use in Spain as the *Demostracion de las Eficaces Virtudes, Nuevamente Descubiertas en las Raices de Dos Plantas de Nueva-España, Especies de Ágave y de Bégonia* (1794). Whatever the merits of the treatment, Balmis's reputation remained intact enough to allow his appointment as head of the royal expedition to vaccinate the Spanish colonies against smallpox from 1803 to 1807.

Other monographs in the Cleveland collections which deal primarily with the medicinal qualities of individual plants or plant groups include Georg Wolfgang Wedel's *Opiologia* (1682), Peter Canvane's *Dissertation on the Oleum Palmae Christi* (circa 1764), William Withering's celebrated *Account of the Foxglove* (1785), and Hipólito Ruiz Lopez's *Quinologia* (1792), as well as medical dissertations such as John M. Walker's *Experimental Inquiry into the Similarity in Virtue between the Cornus Florida*

and *Sericea, and the Cinchona Officinalis of Linnaeus* (1803), Lewis Burwell's *Observations on the Digitalis Purpurea* (1805), and Achille Richard's *Histoire Naturelle et Médicale des Différentes Espèces d'Ipécacuanha* (1820).

FRONTISPIECE. Peter Canvane, *A Dissertation on the Oleum Palmae Christi,* 1764. (GC).

DIGITALIS PURPUREA by James Sowerby. William Withering, *An Account of the Foxglove,* 1785. (CMLA).

A S WE HAVE ALREADY seen in the case of guaiac, the discovery of the New World led to the introduction of new plants and new medicines. The wave of exploration was not confined to the West, however, but extended to Africa and the Orient as well. One of the seminal events in the spread of the new medicinal plants from abroad was the publication in 1574 of a Latin translation and abridgement of Nicolas Monardes' *De Simplicibus Medicamentis Ex Occidentali India Delatis by* Charles L'Ecluse (Clusius) and Garcia da Orta's *Aromatum, et Simplicium aliquot Medicamentorum apud Indos Nascentium Historia* (the latter first published in 1567). This work made available to all of learned Europe the works previously accessible only to the Spanish and Portuguese reading communities.

Monardes was a Spanish doctor. He never visited the New World, but was willing to credibly pass on the tales of newly discovered plants, medicines, and cures brought back by the Spanish explorers without seriously exposing their claims to controlled experimentation. The English version of his account, *Joyfull Newes Out of the New-Found Worlde*, was first published in 1577, but is currently represented in the Cleveland collections by the third edition of 1596.

Garcia da Orta was the son of Spanish Jews who fled to Portugal and nominally accepted Christianity to escape the persecution of the Inquisition. After studying medicine in Spain, and practicing and teaching the subject in Portugal, Orta sailed to Goa in 1534 as the personal physician to M. A. de Sousa, who eventually became Viceroy of Portuguese India. After years of practice in Goa and extensive travel in India and Ceylon, Orta decided to set forth his knowledge of the plants, customs, and medicine of the region in the form of a series of dialogues between himself and a fictitious Dr. Ruano, who represented theoretical knowledge as opposed by the pragmatism of Orta. These dialogues were initially published in Portuguese at Goa in 1563. Although a man of substance in the Portuguese community and known throughout Europe via the medium of Clusius's translation, his position and reputation were not enough to protect his corpse or his family from the Inquisition. His sister was martyred, the rest of his family deported from Goa to Portugal, and his remains exhumed and burned.

Four months after Orta's death, Cristóbal Acosta, a Portuguese soldier and physician landed in Goa. Acosta, whose travels took him to Persia, Malaysia, and perhaps China, as well as India, expanded on Orta's work to produce his *Tractados de las Drogas, y Medicinas de las Indias Orientales* first published in Portuguese in 1578. Like the works of Monardes and Orta, the book gained wider recognition through the Latin abridgement and translation of Clusius which began accompanying those of Monardes and Orta with an edition of 1593.

Another book expanding on the work initially done by Orta was the *De Medicina Indorum* of Jakob de Bondt which was first published posthumously in 1642, and is present in the Cleveland collections in a 1645 edition combining it with Prospero Alpini's *De Medicina Aegyptorum*. In this instance, however, the author was a Dutch physician who was appointed Inspector of Surgeons for the Dutch colonies in India in 1626.

The Dutch are also represented by the handsome twelve volume *Hortus Malabaricus,* produced by a number of authors for Heinrich Adrian van Rheede tot Draakestein, Governor of Malabar for the Dutch East India Company. It was published from 1678 through 1693. Another Dutch work is the sumptuous two volume *Horti Medici Amstelodamensis* of Jan and Caspar Commelin published in 1697 and 1701, which displays the medicinal plants brought back by the Dutch merchants and explorers as grown in the Amsterdam physic garden.

KATOU TSJAKA, engraving by Father Matthieu. Heinrich Adrian von Rheede tot Draakestein, *Hortus Malabaricus,* 1628-1703. (HA).

The Dutch presence in Brazil is reflected by the *Historia Naturalis Brasiliae* of Willem Piso and Georg Markgraf that was first published in 1648. The medical section by Piso, a Dutch physician who accompanied Count Maurice of Nassau to the Dutch colonies in Brazil, is notable as being the first work to distinguish between yaws and syphilis, and the first work to suggest that the best way to maintain the health of Europeans in the tropics was to emulate the lifestyles of the natives. The work also introduced ipecacuanha (or ipecac) to the European materia medica.

The first book published in Europe to be entirely devoted to the flora and fauna of China proper was the *Flora Sinensis* of Michael Boym published in Vienna in 1656. It was based on Boym's observations as a Polish Jesuit missionary in China from 1643 to 1652 and is in the collection at The Holden Arboretum.

The English explorations are represented by a number of works including John Josselyn's *New-Englands Rarities Discovered* which was published in 1672. The work details the natural history of the area around Black Point and Scarborough, Maine, where Josselyn visited his brother in 1638 and 1663. It includes accounts of the medical and alimentary uses of various plants and animals of the area.

Also appearing in 1672 was William Hughes' *The American Physitian* in which Hughes describes the plants and their medicinal uses as observed while serving as a sailor in Jamaica.

Later, and reflecting a different part of the British Empire, is *A Catalogue of Indian Medicinal Plants and Drugs* written by John Fleming, the president of the Bengal Medical Service, and published in Calcutta in 1810.

ALOE SUCCOTRINA ANGUSTI FOLIO SPINOSA FLORE PURPUREO. Caspar Commelin, *Horti Medici Amstelodamensis,* 1701.

YA TA, woodcut. Michael Boym, ***Flora Sinensis,*** 1656. (HA).

THE SASSAFRAS, woodcut. John Josselyn, ***New Englands Rarities Discovered,*** 1672. (CMLA).

ENGRAVED TITLE PAGE. Willem Piso and Georg Markgraf, ***Historia Naturalis Brasiliae,*** 1648. (HA).

THIS SEEMS AN APPRO-
priate time to turn to a discussion of
the English herbals and their continental in-
fluences and parallels as represented in the collections. We have already mentioned the *Grete
Herball* published in 1526. The next major English herbal was William Turner's *New Herbal*
or *Herbal*. The first part was initially published
in 1561; the complete work in 1568. Turner,
like the German Fathers of Botany, was a product of the Reformation. A Non-Conformist
who was a pupil of Nicholas Ridley and an as-
sociate of Hugh Latimer, he was jailed for two
years, exiled from England and his books
banned under Henry VIII. He was exiled again
with his books banned and burned under Mary.
Turner's years of exile were productive, however, since they were spent in extensive European travels where he made the acquaintance
of most of the major naturalists and obtained

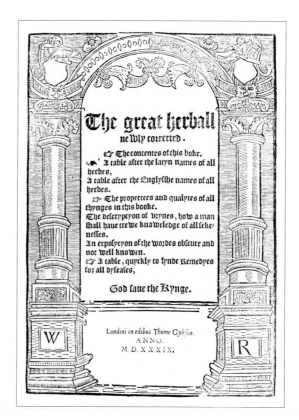

TITLE PAGE. *The Grete Herball,* 1526.

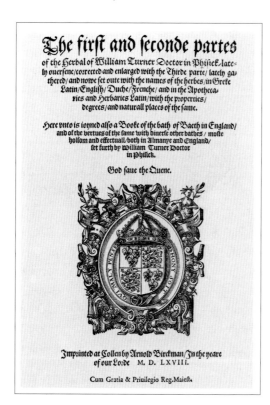

TITLE PAGE. William Turner, *Herbal,*
1561-1568. (CMLA).

his medical degree. His non-botanic efforts were
rewarded under Edward VI by his appointment
as physician and chaplain to the Lord Protec-
tor Edmund Duke of Somerset and as Preben-
dary of York and Dean of Wells. Although he
lost these posts with the accession of Mary,
the religious appointments were restored under Elizabeth I, to whom he dedicated the first
complete edition of the herbal.

The work is of major importance as the first
herbal in English to be written by an Englishman. The tone of the work is sometimes as com-
bative as his religious works, but his
assertiveness was supported by a substantial
body of research, observation, knowledge, and
scientific attitude that have led some people to
dub him the Father of English Botany. Unfortunately, although the work was not confined
to English plants, Turner's choice of publishing it in English, for the benefit of the many
English physicians and apothecaries whom
Turner felt could not read Latin or Greek, pre-

cluded the work from wide circulation on the continent despite the fact that all but the first edition of the first part were printed in Cologne.

The next important herbal to be printed in England was the *Stirpium Adversaria Nova* of 1571. The book was composed by Pierre Pena and Matthias de L'Obel, who came originally from Provence and Lille and studied medicine and botany together at Montpellier under the noted botanist Guillaume Rondelet. After Rondelet's death in 1566, the pair came to England where they botanized throughout the country and produced the *Stirpium*.

Both eventually returned to the continent where Pena went on to become physician to King Henry III of France. L'Obel went to Antwerp where he saw his subsequent productions through the press of Christopher Plantin. He became physician to William the Silent, the Stadholder of the Low Countries, and after

ENGRAVED TITLE PAGE. Pierre Pena and Matthias de L'Obel, *Stirpium Adversaria Nova*, 1570-1571. (CMLA).

William's assassination in 1584, returned to England where he became superintendent of Lord Zouche's estate at Hackney and was eventually appointed Botanicus Regius to King James I of England.

Plantin bought 800 copies of the *Stirpium* which he reissued with a new title page and additional material under the title *Nova Stirpium Adversaria*, published as a companion volume to L'Obel's *Plantarum seu Stirpium Adversaria* in 1576.

The works of Rembert Dodoens, the famous Flemish botanist and physician, form the basis for the next important English herbals. Dodoens served at various times as city physician to his hometown of Mechlin, as physician to Emperor Maximilian II, and as professor of medicine at Leyden. He entered into a business arrangement about 1552 with Jean Loë, a publisher of Antwerp, to provide the text of an illustrated herbal which was published in 1554 as the Flemish *Cruydeboek*. Although the Cleveland collections do not have a copy of the Flemish work, they do have a copy of the French translation done by Dodoens's friend Clusius and published as *Histoire des Plantes* (1557) by Loë. This French edition and a late "Douch" edition served in turn as the basis for Henry Lyte's English translation which appeared as the *Niewe Herball* in 1578 and was the last of Dodoens's works to be published by Loë.

Lyte's translation, an English translation by Robert Priest of Dodoens's *Stirpium Historiae Pemptades Sex*, a revised and collected edition of most of Dodoens's botanical writings first published by Plantin in 1583, and the works of Turner, Tabernaemontanus, Pena, and L'Obel served as the basis for one of the most celebrated and enduring English herbals, *The Herball, or Generall Historie of Plants*. Written by John Gerard, it has a publication date of 1597.

The author was an English barber-surgeon, herbalist, and horticulturist, who at various times served as superintendent of gardens to William Cecil, first Baron Burghley, at his residences in the Strand and in Herefordshire, and as curator of the physic garden established by the College of Physicians of London in 1586.

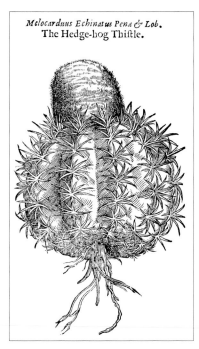

Melocarduus Echinatus Penæ & Lob.
The Hedge-hog Thiftle.

THE HEDGE-HOG THISTLE, woodcut. John Gerard, as revised by Thomas Johnson, ***The Herball,*** 1633. (GC).

Despite its celebrity, the work suffered from errors of identification, faulty Latin, and incorrect illustrations, over a thousand of which were corrected by L'Obel at the publisher's request before Gerard stopped the revision. Highly uneven in nature, the work portrays items such as Gerard's credulous account of the barnacle goose while at other times it provides important information such as the first illustration of the potato (albeit with a highly misleading account of its origins). The work was finally revised by Thomas Johnson, a London apothecary who was assisted by John Goodyer and others. The errors were corrected to such a degree that the second edition of ***The Herball,*** which appeared in 1633, is often referred to as the ***Gerard Emaculata.***

Four years prior to the publication of the second edition of Gerard's herbal, John Parkinson, a London apothecary who became apothecary to King James I and was appointed Botanicus Regius Primarius by Charles I, published a horticultural work on the flower garden, kitchen garden, and orchard. It was entitled ***Paradisi in Sole Paradisus Terrestris.*** At the same time, Parkinson began writing a companion volume covering herbs and predominantly medicinal plants that is believed to have been largely completed by 1635. Its publication was delayed until 1640, however, owing to the expense of its size and illustrations and the overwhelming popularity of Johnson's revision of Gerard. The ***Theatrum Botanicum,*** as the work was titled, represented a primitive scientific classification, with the plants described grouped and divided into 17 tribes such as sweet smelling plants and purgatives.

From the time of the German Fathers of Botany, the authors of herbals for the most part appear to display certain common characteristics including a background in medicine and/or pharmacy, an interest in botany and/or horticulture, and a deep seated religious conviction (although the faith varies). In many of these authors there is an expression of the desire to unlock the secret of God's creation through the study of botany and medicinal plants, yet for other writers the intent of the deity is both open and manifest. One such

The Garden of pleaſant Flowers.

A PAGE OF DAFFODIL WOODCUTS. John Parkinson, ***Paradisi in Sole,*** 1629. (CMLA).

writer is Timothy Bright, the British physician who was the great-grandfather of William Congreve, the Restoration playwright. In his *A Treatise wherein Is Declared the Sufficiencie of English Medicines* and *A Collection of Medicines Growing . . . within Our English Climate* first published in 1580, Bright expounds his view that Providence furnishes the natural remedies within each country for all diseases within that country. He presents the view with such fervor in the case of England that the combined works are often described as a piece of medical nationalism. The copy present in the Cleveland collections is the second edition of 1615.

For others the will of God was equally manifest but more universal with cures for diseases made apparent through the doctrine of signatures. The doctrine is supposed to have originated in the writings of Theophrastus Bombastus von Hohenheim, the Swiss alchemist and physician better known as Paracelsus, although it has obvious Platonic and Neo-Platonic roots. Briefly stated, it holds that God has revealed the virtues of various plants by their characteristics, meaning in its simplest form that plants whose forms resemble snakes are good for treating snakebites, various plants whose leaves or roots are shaped like the heart are good for treating heart ailments, etc. Paracelsus discussed relatively few plants, however, being more concerned with his chemical and alchemical theories. The fullest development of the doctrine was left to Giambattista della Porta, a Neapolitan physicist, alchemist, and dramatist, whose writings include plays, works on the secrets of nature, memory and mnemonic devices, cryptography, optics, and human physiognomy. Porta expounded the theory as it pertained to plants in the *Phytognomonica* first published in 1588 and represented in the Cleveland collections by the second edition of 1591. According to Porta, long-lived plants would promote long-life, scaly plants would cure scaly diseases, and so forth.

Porta then took the doctrine of signatures one step farther and applied it to the human physiognomy in his *De Humana Physiognomia* which is regrettably not in the Cleveland collections. In that work he held that bodily form reflected character and spiritual qualities. These works, combined with the supposed interest in magic of the Accademia Secretorum Naturae which

WOODCUT showing the common signs of scaled plants, snakes, and fish. Giambattista della Porta, *Phytognomonica*, 1591. (HA).

he founded, resulted in the Inquisition banning his books from 1592 to 1598.

In England, the chief proponent of the doctrine of signatures was William Coles or Cole, the English botanist and simpler, who used the theory throughout his herbal, *Adam in Eden*, first published in 1657. The doctrine, as well as botanical astrology, are also referred to in the introduction of Robert Lovell's *Pambotanologia* first published in 1659 and present in the Cleveland collections in the second edition of 1665. Lovell, who apparently practiced medicine without ever taking a medical degree, produced an omnium-gatherum (a miscellaneous collection) of information on plants from other works and arranged alphabetically by English names. Although no information on signatures or astrology is given under the discussion of individual plants, the introduction contains both a list of plants endowed with signatures and a list of plants connected with the planets and the zodiac.

The foremost of the English astrological botanists was Nicholas Culpeper. Culpeper's herbal first appeared in 1652 under the title of *The English Physitian*, while the earliest edition in the Cleveland collections is that of 1662 entitled the *English Physician Enlarged*. Briefly stated, Culpeper believed that each disease was ruled by a planet or constellation and could be cured either by sympathy through the use of a plant ruled by the same planet or by antipathy through the use of an herb ruled by an opposing planet. The book was intended as a populist work to be used by the general public rather than physicians, and as such it was confined to plants generally found in England. Earlier Culpeper had won the enmity of the London medical establishment with his unauthorized English translation of the *Pharmacopoeia Londinensis*. This was the official pharmacopoeia of the College of Physicians of London that was first published as *A Physicall Directory* in 1649. It is present in the Cleveland collections as the *Pharmacopoeia Londinensis* of 1653 and 1669.

Other works in the collections which are aimed at making medicines available to the

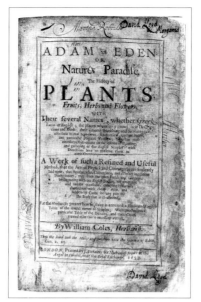

TITLE PAGE. William Coles, *Adam in Eden,* 1657. (CMLA).

masses include the 1561 edition of Hieronymus Brunschwig's *A Most Excellent and Perfecte Homish Apothecarye* published in Cologne and usually found bound with copies of Turner's *Herbal* from the same publisher. Along the same lines are the numerous editions of Samuel Auguste André David Tissot's *Avis au Peuple Sur sa Santé* which was first published in 1761 and translated into English in 1765 as *Advice to the People in General with Regard to Their Health*.

Another English translator of the *Pharmacopoeia Londinensis* was William Salmon whose edition appeared in 1691. Salmon is generally regarded as a mountebank who practiced medicine, chemistry, alchemy, and pharmacy, although he used the titles of M.D. and professor of physick in his works and legal documents. He amassed a 3000 volume library including many of the medical classics, and wrote with sufficient erudition in some of his medical works to evoke objections from his critics that the books were ghost-written. Among the books by Salmon in the Cleveland collections are the third edition of his *Family-Dictionary* (1705), a combination cookbook, herbal, book on perfume making, and book on wines and ales, and the first edition of his *Botanologia* published in 1710. The latter is Salmon's largely derivative herbal devoted to English medicinal plants and ornamental flowers.

Another controversial author is Sir John Hill, the British apothecary, gardener, physician, editor, translator, and sometime actor, who was awarded the Order of Vasa in 1774 by the Swedish King for his 26 volume *The Vegetable System* published from 1759 through 1775. A man of real ability and genius, his achievements have long been undercut by his egotism and the accounts given of him by the enemies he made through his own satirical attacks on the learned societies and personalities of the period. While this work is not in the Cleveland collections, others by him are. Hill's first appearance in the Cleveland collections is as the editor of the fourth edition (1748) of the English translation of Pierre Pomet's *A Compleat History of Drugs*. Hill's three volume *A General Natural History* published from 1748 to 1752 describes animals, vegetables, and minerals, noting their medicinal values and uses whenever relevant. (The volume entitled *History of Plants* introduced the new plant classification system of Linnaeus to England and is best remembered for this reason). A more detailed account of the medicinal uses of various substances is given in Hill's *History of the Materia Medica* first published in 1751, while a briefer account of medicinal plants aimed at the general public first appeared in 1754 as *The Useful Family Herbal*. The latter is present here in the sixth edition published in 1812 as *The Family Herbal*. *The British Herbal*, on the other hand, published from 1756 through 1757 in small format copies and from 1757 through 1758 in large format copies, was aimed more at the serious botanist and taxonomist. In it, Hill rejects the artificial system of Linnaeus in favor of a system relying more heavily on the forms of corollas and gynoeciums in its analysis of British plants.

Hill seems to be one of the main authorities cited in *A New and Compleat Body of Practical Botanic Physic* published in 1791. The work was written by Edward Baylis, an English physician who practiced in Clifton a suburb of Bristol, where he also maintained a physic garden. It is mainly derivative with a narrative consisting primarily of accounts of the medicinal uses of plants.

ONE OF THE MOST poignant tales in the history of herbals is that of Elizabeth Blackwell and her curious herbal. The story begins with Elizabeth's husband, Alexander Blackwell, a distinguished scholar in Greek, Latin, and French, who worked as a corrector for a printer before illegally setting himself up in the printer's trade without undergoing the mandatory apprenticeship. After being convicted on this count, he was subsequently jailed for bankruptcy. In order to free her husband from jail, Elizabeth set herself up across from the Chelsea physick garden and began copying medicinal plants for an herbal in which she engraved both the pictures and the text. *A Curious Herbal* appeared in two volumes issued between 1737 and 1739. The Cleveland collections contain a variety of issues among its copies including the original issue by Samuel Harding, later issues from John Nourse, and the pirated letterpress edition of part of

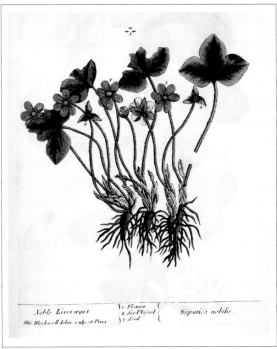

NOBLE LIVERWORT by Elizabeth Blackwell.
Elizabeth Blackwell,
A Curious Herbal, 1737-1739. (CMLA).

volume one that was the object of a successful Chancery suit. The work enjoyed the patronage of a number of the leading physicians and scientists of its day and had its sales helped by receiving the official approbation of the Royal College of Physicians of London resulting in the rescue of Alexander from his impecunious position. As is the case with the lives of many of the authors of herbals and botanical works, the story does not have a happy ending. Alexander Blackwell went on to become director of improvements for the Duke of Chambros, only to leave the position under a cloud; he then went to Sweden where he served as an agricultural expert but got involved in politics and ended up being executed for treason to the Swedish crown.

Also in the collections is the third century, as each section of a hundred plates and their accompanying text is termed, of Christoph Jakob Trew's expansion of Elizabeth Blackwell's herbal (1757). This **Herbarium Blackwellianum** was issued from 1757 through 1765. The expanded descriptions are the work of Trew, G. R. Böhmer, and E. G. Bose. The plates by Nikolaus Friedrich Eisenberger add details of flower parts, fruits, etc., which were not included in Mrs. Blackwell's originals.

Another engraved herbal is the **Botanicum Medicinale** written and engraved by Timothy Sheldrake. Sheldrake, who had studied drawing and painting as a youth, had an unsuccessful career as a saddler, after which he bought a distiller's office and set about learning about simples, plants, and drugs. The result of this effort, apart from its

effects on Sheldrake's distilling business, was the preparation of the highly ornate herbal which was originally issued in parts from 1756 through 1757 and is present here in the second issue of circa 1768.

The need to standardize medicines in terms of both the identification of drugs and the consistency of formulation of compound medicines led to the creation of official pharmacopoeias aimed at the medical and pharmaceutical trades. As we have mentioned earlier, the first of these official pharmacopoeias was that created by Cordus which eventually became the standard for most of Germany. In England, the two main official pharmacopoeias were those produced

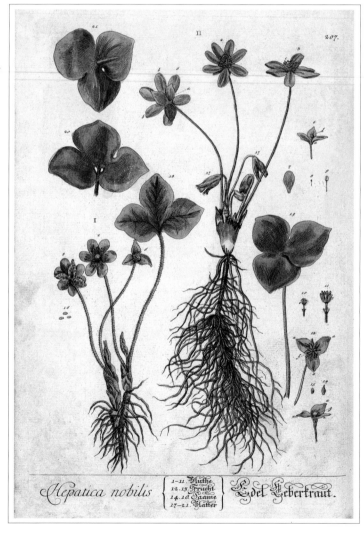

HEPATICA NOBILIBUS by Nikolaus Friedrich Eisenberger. Johann Christoph Trew, **Herbarium Blackwellianum,** 1757-1765.

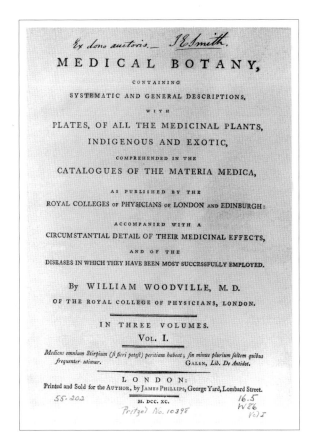

TITLE PAGE from a presentation copy with signature of James Edward Smith. William Woodville, *Medical Botany*, 1790. (HA).

respectively for the Royal College of Physicians of London and the Royal College of Physicians of Edinburgh. While these works standardized the medicines dispensed, they did not attempt to illustrate or describe the plants of the materia medica in the manner which the herbals had done. In order to provide more modern illustrations and descriptions of the most used medicinal plants, a number of works appeared aimed at supplementing the official pharmacopoeias. The earliest English work created for this purpose in the Cleveland collections is the *Medical Botany* of William Woodville which was first published from 1790 through 1795. Woodville was an English Quaker physician and botanist who studied under William Cullen, the distinguished lecturer and writer on the materia medica at Edinburgh. A copy at The Holden Arboretum is of particular interest since it was

presented by the author to James E. Smith, the founder and first president of the Linnean Society.

A somewhat later work in the same vein, but incorporating the plants of the Dublin pharmacopoeia, as well as those of the London and Edinburgh pharmacopoeias, is the anonymous *Medical Botany* first published in 1819-1821. It is present in the Cleveland collections in the second edition of 1819-1821. Yet another anonymous medical botany was the *Flora Medica* published from 1829 through 1830. George Spratt, a British surgeon-accoucheur, acknowledged the work as his in his *Medico-Botanical Pocket-Book* (circa 1830).

STRYCHNOS NUX VOMICA. William Woodville, *Medical Botany*, 1821-1822. (CMLA).

More unconventional medicine makes its appearance in Charles Whitlaw's **Whitlaw's New Medical Discoveries with a Defence of the Linnaean Doctrine** (1829). Apart from the first English translation of Linnaeus's **Materia Medica** (originally published in Latin in 1749 and 1763) which occupies the second volume, the work is mainly a rambling promotional work for Whitlaw's patented "vapour-bath." Whitlaw claimed that this device, when used with processed herbs, would obviate the need for the use of "narcotic, acrid, and corrosive poisons" in the treatment of diseases. In the course of his narrative we learn that Whitlaw was born in Scotland, studied landscape gardening at the botanical garden in Edinburgh, then went to the United States, Canada, the "Leeward Indies", and Mexico, where he earned a living as a landscape gardener, medicinal plant collector, and nurseryman. According to this account he attended lectures on chemistry, medicine, agriculture and horticulture during the winters. Through his observations, he came to the conclusion that the vegetable medicines used by the American Indians, particularly as used in a steam bath, were more effective than the then current materia medica with its heavy emphasis on mercury and other inorganic medicines. The doctrine of herbal medicine espoused by Whitlaw appears to be a combination of the ancient humoral theory of medicine and a variant of the doctrine of signatures, apparently originating with Linnaeus's **Materia Medica**.

These same doctrines of botanical medicine are also put forward by Thomas Green in his **Universal Herbal** first published between 1816 and 1820. These doctrines are joined by another familiar one that says that nature provides cures for all native illnesses within a given country. Although the herbal proper is relatively innocuous and mainly devoted to plant description, with minor comments on the medicinal and economic benefits of the plants, the preliminary matter is sometimes vitriolic in its attacks on apothecaries who use their foreign medicines to turn little disorders into great ones. Instead, the work gives detailed instructions for gathering and preparing one's own herbs. Unfortunately, the work goes a bit overboard in its espousal of the Linnaean doctrine by its suggestion that everyone should experiment with untried plants of the same characteristics of fruit and flower to find more effective medicines — a suggestion which conceivably could have led to disastrous results.

To round out the discussion of the English herbals present in Cleveland, passing reference must be made to Robert John Thornton's **A New Family Herbal** first published in 1810. It was similar to the family herbal of Hill but

SOLANUM DULCUMARA by George Spratt. George Spratt, **Flora Medica,** [1827-] 1829-1830. (CMLA).

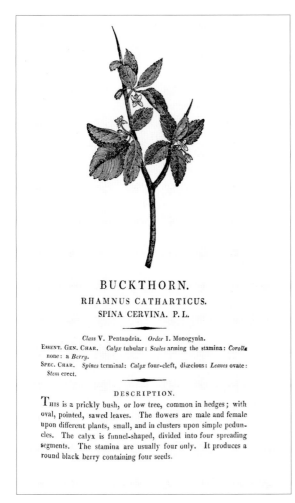

BUCKTHORN.

RHAMNUS CATHARTICUS.

SPINA CERVINA. P. L.

———

Class V. Pentandria.   *Order* I. Monogynia.

ESSENT. GEN. CHAR.   *Calyx* tubular: *Scales* arming the stamina: *Corolla* none: a *Berry*.

SPEC. CHAR.   *Spines* terminal: *Calyx* four-cleft, dioecious: *Leaves* ovate: *Stem* erect.

———

DESCRIPTION.

THIS is a prickly bush, or low tree, common in hedges; with oval, pointed, sawed leaves. The flowers are male and female upon different plants, small, and in clusters upon simple peduncles. The calyx is funnel-shaped, divided into four spreading segments. The stamina are usually four only. It produces a round black berry containing four seeds.

BUCKTHORN, wood engraving by Thomas Bewick after John Henderson. Robert John Thornton, *A New Family Herbal,* 1810.

graced with Thomas Bewick's only botanical wood engravings.

In the United States, both before and after independence, the medical and pharmaceutical community relied heavily on books imported from England and the continent. Sometimes rather than simply reprinting a foreign book, the work was adapted to the practices of the American community as was the case with *The American Dispensatory* of John Redman Coxe published at Philadelphia in 1806. It was based on the second edition of *The Edinburgh New Dispensatory*.

The credit for the first herbal of indigenous drugs designed for the former British North American colonies goes to Samuel Stearns, a colonial physician whose Tory sympathies created numerous problems for him both during and after the American Revolution. His landmark work entitled simply *The American Herbal* was published at Walpole, New Hampshire, in 1801 and focused on the organic and inorganic materia medica indigenous to both North and South America.

Three years earlier, in 1798, Benjamin Smith Barton published the first part of his three part *Collections for an Essay towards a Materia Medica of the United States*. Barton initially became interested in native medicines when he observed those used by the American Indians while serving on the team which surveyed the western boundary of Pennsylvania. After receiving medical training at Philadelphia, Edinburgh, and London, Barton finally received his M.D. from Göttingen. He then returned to Philadelphia where he combined his medical career with a teaching career, serving at various times as professor of natural history and botany, professor of materia medica, and professor of the theory and practice of medicine at the College of Philadelphia (now the Univeristy of Pennsylvania). The first edition of the *Collections* to contain all three parts in a single volume was published in 1810. It is the edition present in Cleveland.

While Barton collected the materials for a native materia medica, it was left to James Thacher, an American physician best known as America's first medical historian, to take these materials and combine them with materials previously published in the *Pharmacopoeia of the Massachusetts Medical Society* to produce *The American New Dispensatory* also first published in 1810.

Although Thacher fulfilled the need of knowing how to use the materia medica collected by Barton, the need still existed for an illustrated work to aid in the identification of the plants cited by Barton. Two men, both graduates of the University of Pennsylvania, each set out independently to remedy this situation. William Paul Crillon Barton, the nephew of Benjamin Smith Barton, was a physician who at various times served as professor of botany at the University of Pennsylvania, instructor in materia medica at Jefferson Medical School, and first head of the Bureau of Medicine and Surgery of the United States Navy. His *Vegetable Materia Medica of the United States* with 50 illustrative plates was published from 1817 through 1819. At the same time, Jacob Bigelow published his *American Medical Botany* with 60 plates which continued publication through 1821. Bigelow was a physician who was one of the co-deliverers of the first botany lectures at Harvard and who served there at various times as professor of materia medica in the Medical School and as Rumford professor in the application of science to the useful arts.

Since both of these works were on the expensive side owing to the number of engraved colored plates involved, Samuel Constantine Rafinesque, the peripatetic Sicilian born naturalist, set out to produce a more affordable work with more illustrations — the cost being kept down by using what appear to be woodcuts printed in a single color. The result was the *Medical Flora* published between 1828 and 1830 which contained illustrations of all of the plants appearing in Barton and Bigelow plus 25 others.

The most important event of the period in the United States, however, was the creation of

the first national official pharmacopoeia in an effort to standardize drugs throughout the still-young country. The need for a national pharmacopoeia created with the authority of all the medical societies and medical schools of the United States was first proposed to the New York County Medical Society in 1817 by

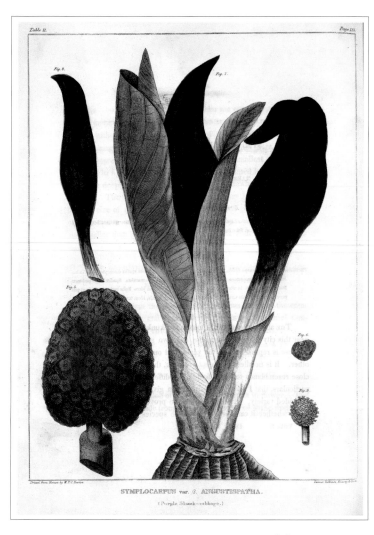

SYMPLOCARPUS VAR. ANGUSTISPATHA engraved by Tanner, Valance, Kearny and Co. after W. P. C. Barton. William Paul Crillon Barton, *Vegetable Materia Medica of the United States,* 1817-1818[-1819]. (CMLA).

Lyman Spaulding. A consensus for the need of such a work was reached and delegates were elected at four regional conventions to form regional pharmacopoeias and elect delegates to the national convention to be held January 1, 1820, in Washington, D.C. The result of the

PHYTOLACCA DECANDRA, hand-colored line engraving. Jacob Bigelow, *American Medical Botany,* 1817. (CMLA).

PHYTOLACCA DECANDRA, color-printed aquatint engraving. Jacob Bigelow, *American Medical Botany,* 1817-1820 [-1821]. (CMLA).

national convention was the adoption of a combination of the pharmacopoeias submitted by the northern and middle regions with certain additions to form the ***Pharmacopoeia of the United States*** published in 1820. It served as the standard throughout the country until 1830 when another convention was convened.

There were also, of course, authors somewhat removed from the mainstreams of American medical and pharmaceutical practice producing herbals and alternative medical systems. One such person was John Monroe, a native of New Hampshire. Monroe claimed to have studied under several physicians and to have read medical classics before going into the wilds and studying under a native American who was "regularly bred a physician in the medical department of the Philadelphia University."

After this he studied for a half year under a German physician. The result of this unique medical education was the publication in 1824 of ***The American Botanist, and Family Physician.*** It was a compilation of native American remedies based partly on Stearns, but mostly original in its derivation from the medicine of the American Indians.

Another American work which requires brief mention is the 1827 "first edition" of ***Steward's Healing Art*** by William Steward. It is actually a large expansion of a pamphlet which originally appeared in 1812. The herbal section, which is slender on description, is organized by disease rather than by plant groups, with all herbs used to treat a given condition gathered in one place.

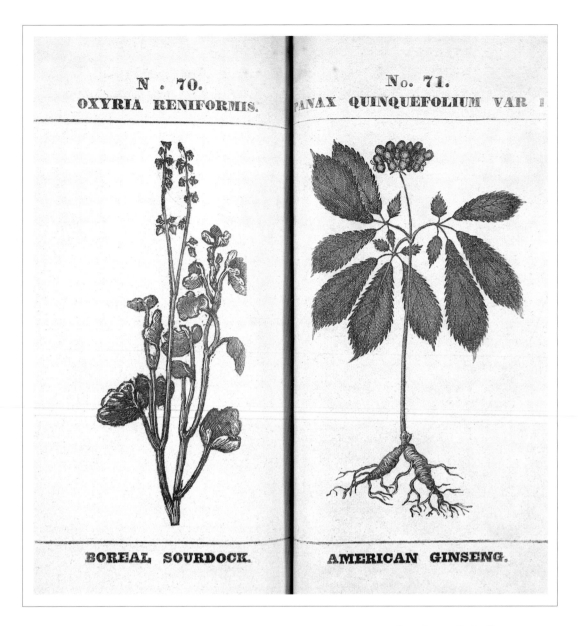

N . 70.
OXYRIA RENIFORMIS.

No. 71.
PANAX QUINQUEFOLIUM VAR 1.

BOREAL SOURDOCK.

AMERICAN GINSENG.

OXYRIA VENIFORMIS AND PANAX QUINQUEFOLIUM VAR. 1. Constantine Samuel Rafinesque, *Medical Flora,* 1828-1830. (CMLA).

The most famous of the alternative "physicians", however, was Samuel Thomson, the New England creator of a system usually referred to as botanic medicine or Thomsonianism. In essence Thomson believed that all illnesses are produced by cold and that any treatment which increases inward heat would hasten recovery. Although the Thomsonian pharmacopoeia featured a number of herbs, Thomson's mainstays appear to have been treatments using lobelia, cayenne pepper, and steam. Thomson patented his system and allowed its use by anyone who would pay him a fee. The system was generally opposed by the regular physicians of the day, and Thomson himself was jailed for six weeks and at one point tried for murder. Nonetheless, the system was looked on with a more sympathetic view by some leading physicians, including Benjamin Rush and Benjamin Waterhouse, and is generally regarded as having a major medical and pharmaceutical influence during the first half of the nineteenth century. The movement is represented in the collections by several editions of Thomson's

TITLE PAGE. Charles Miles, *A New and Improved System of Medical Botanical Practice*, 1829.

Narrative of the Life and Medical Discoveries of Samuel Thomson including one which may be a first edition printed in 1822. There is also an 1825 edition of Thomson's *New Guide to Health* and a rambling defence of the system by Samuel Robinson, an Ohio practitioner, published as *A Course of Fifteen Lectures, on Medical Botany* (1829).

One final medical botanical work, the 1829 *A New and Improved System of Medical Botanical Practice* of Charles Miles, needs to be mentioned, not because of any major influence on the American medical scene, but because of its importance as the earliest medical work known to have been published in Cleveland, Ohio. Miles, who according to his own account practiced all over the country, sets forth a doctrine calling for the maintenance of "a proper energy and excitement" in the nervous system and the preservation of an equilibrium in the circulating fluids. His account includes a section on botanic medicine, with the plants organized according to their medicinal properties. as well as a section on surgery.

CHAPTER II

Botanical and Scientific Works

THE RECORDED SCIENCE OF BOTANY begins with *Historia Plantarum* and *De Causis Plantarum* written by Theophrastus of Eresos in the third century B.C. Theophrastus was a pupil of Plato and Aristotle and inherited Aristotle's library and botanical garden. Best remembered for his botanical works, Theophrastus was a prodigious author in a wide variety of fields, although only a few of the over 200 books credited to him survive. He is noted for his detailed examination and description of plants and his initial attempt at plant classification that divided all plants into trees, shrubs, undershrubs, and herbs. It is on the basis of these works that Theophrastus is often cited as the father of botany. His works are represented in the Cleveland collections by *De Historia et Causis Plantarum Libri Quindecim*, a 1529 edition of the Latin translation of Theophrastus's two works, originally done by Theodore Gaza for Pope Nicholas V in the 1450's; *Dell'Historia delle Piante*, an Italian translation by Michelangelo Biondo of the *Historia Plantarum* published in 1549; and *De*

Historia Plantarum Libri Decem, featuring the Gaza Latin translation along with the Greek text edited and annotated by Johannes Badaeus à Stapel published in 1644.

Apart from Dioscorides and Nicander, whom we have already discussed in the chapter on herbals and medical botanical works, the other main classical botanical writer was Caius Plinius Secundus, more commonly known in English as Pliny the Elder. Pliny was a Roman soldier, statesman, and the author of seven works (most of which dealt with rhetoric or military history). The only one of these works to survive is the massive *Historia Naturalis*. Pliny's work on natural history dating from the first century A.D. is regarded as the oldest surviving encyclopedia. The botanical portion is concentrated in books 12 through 27 of the 37 book work and deals with agriculture, horticulture, and medical botany. Although the first printed edition dates from 1469 and the first illustrated printed edition from 1513, the earliest edition in the Cleveland collections is an unillustrated edition of 1517. All told the Cleveland collections contain five editions of the work including *The Historie of the World*, the first English translation of the work published in 1601.

The medieval view of botany is reflected in the collections in the works of two later encyclopedists. Vincent of Beauvais, a thirteenth century French Dominican, is represented by an edition of the *Speculum Doctrinale* published in Strassburg circa 1477. This work, which is one part of his larger work known as the *Speculum Maius*, derives its name from its central premise that by instruction, *doctrina*, man can rise from the original sin of Adam. It covers a wide variety of learned disciplines including domestic science, agriculture, and medicine.

The second medieval encyclopedia in the collections is a 1485 edition of the *De Proprietatibus Rerum* of Bartholomaeus Anglicus. The author, although as his name implies of English birth, was educated in France where he served as professor of philosophy at Paris until 1230 when he was sent to Saxony at the request of the General of the Friars Minor (Franciscans). The work is organized along the lines of the great chain of being working down from the first section on God so that it finally reaches its treatment of trees and plants in section 17. It was probably the most popular of the medieval encyclopedias because of its relatively compact form.

The medieval period was dominated by the concept of *auctoritas*, the notion that the main duty of the scholar was to learn by rote all that had been said by the ancients and that these concepts were not to be questioned. The main authority in the field of botany was Pliny since, while Latin was universal in the learned community, relatively few scholars had the ability to read Greek and even fewer had ready access to manuscripts of Theophrastus or Dioscorides. The advent of the Renaissance in Italy saw a revival of classical studies that challenged this concept. Niccolo Leoniceno, the Italian Humanist and physician, was one of the new wave of scholars. In 1494, he published a work, preserved in the Cleveland collections in its 1509 edition under the title of *De Plinii & Plurium Aliorum Medicina Erroribus*, in which he demonstrated that there were botanical and syntactical errors in the writings of Pliny, Avicenna, and Serapion. Many of these were scribal in nature involving the mistranscription of words from Greek sources into Pliny's Latin account. The work was revolutionary in nature since it undermined the accepted botanical authority by demonstrating that it was not error free.

The works of Leoniceno and others opened the door to a revived form of scholarship based upon original scientific observation and investigation. An example has already been discussed in the previous chapter, where we saw that Hieronymus Bock and Valerius Cordus, through detailed descriptions of their original scientific examinations of plants, laid the groundwork for modern phytography. Other works of this nature include that of Jean Ruel, a French physician and canon of Notre Dame in Paris, who took the botanical writings of the ancients and reorganized the matter into the *De Natura Stirpium* published in Paris in 1536. The work comprised a textbook of botany written in Latin and aimed at a scholarly audience. It included detailed descriptions of all the plants known to Ruel and a section that defined the Latin descriptive terminology of plant parts. Charles Estienne, the Renaissance scholar and member of the famous French printing family, is represented in Cleveland by his *De Latinis et Graecis Nominibus Arborum, Fruticum, Herbarum, Piscium & Avium Liber* (1544). This early dictionary gives the names of plants, birds, and fish in Greek, Latin, and French accompanied by descriptions and citations.

The first original botanical textbook of the sixteenth century was the *De Plantis Libris XVI* of Andrea Cesalpino first published in 1583. Cesalpino was an Italian botanist and physician who succeeded Luca Ghini as professor of medicine and director of the botanical garden at the University of Pisa. He later became physician to Pope Clement VIII and was made a professor of the Sapienza. The work was one of the first to aim at a systematic classification of plants going beyond the basic groupings established by Theophrastus by creating subgroups based upon single, bipartite, tripartite, quadripartite, and multipartite fruits.

Freed from the boundaries of the medieval concept of *auctoritas*, botanists of varying degrees of training set out with unbridled enthusiasm in the sixteenth century to find, study, describe, and arrange the flora of foreign lands and their own figurative back yards.

Pierre Belon was a French apothecary, naturalist, and licentiate in medicine whose travels from 1546 to 1550 provided the material for his *Observations de Plusieurs Singularitez et Choses Memorables Trouvees en Grece, Asie, Judée, Arabie & Autres Pays Etranges*. This account of the peoples, customs, flora, and fauna of the countries visited is represented in the Cleveland collections by the fourth edition published in 1588. A pioneer of comparative anatomy and of the classification of fish and birds, Belon's purely botanical work is reflected in his *De Arboribus Coniferis* of 1553, one of the earliest monographs devoted to a single grouping of plants.

Jean Du Choul was another French naturalist and apothecary. His *De Varia Quercus Historia* and *Pylati Montis Descriptio,* published in 1555, constitute the earliest monographs devoted entirely to oaks and a local flora for Mt. Pilate near Lucerne, Switzerland.

Prospero Alpini, by contrast, was another traveling botanist, fascinated by the exotic plants of foreign lands, and in his capacity as physician to Giorgio Emo, the Venetian consul to Cairo, traveled to Egypt, Cyprus, and Crete. On his return from his travels, he was appointed reader in simples (noncompound medicines) at the University of Padua, and much later in his career became director of the Padua botanical garden.

Alpini's *De Plantis Aegypti* (1592), along with his *Liber de Balsamo*, is the first major treatment of Egyptian botany. It is cast in the form of a dialogue between Alpini and Melchiore Guilando, who had supervised his medical degree. The book is credited with the first European descriptions of the coffee bush, banana, and baobab. Also in the collections is Alpini's *De Plantis Exoticis Libri Duo* that was published posthumously in 1627 and is mainly concerned with plants originally observed in Crete.

The flora of the low countries was extensively described by Rembert Dodoens, a Flemish physician who took up botany relatively late in life. He is first represented in the Cleveland collections by a copy of his *Histoire des Plantes* published in 1557. This was a French translation by Charles de L'Ecluse (Clusius) of Dodoens's Flemish *Cruydeboeck* first published three years earlier. Dodoens is also represented in Cleveland by the second edition of his *Frumentorum, Leguminum, et Herbarum Historia*, his study of grains, vegetables, and marsh and water vegetation; the 1568 first edition and the 1569 revised edition of the *Florum et Nonnullarum Herbarum Historia*, his account of ornamental and fragrant plants; and the 1583 first edition of Dodoens's *Stirpium Historiae Pemptades Sex*. This latter book represents the collected works of Dodoens, revised and rearranged by the author and with new material added. Generally believed to be the most common of Dodoens's works, it is divided into six sections termed *pemptades* because each section contained five books.

As we have already noted in the previous chapter, the early botanical works of Dodoens were produced at the instigation of Jean Loë, an Antwerp printer who had noticed the market for botanical works made evident by the numerous editions in various languages of

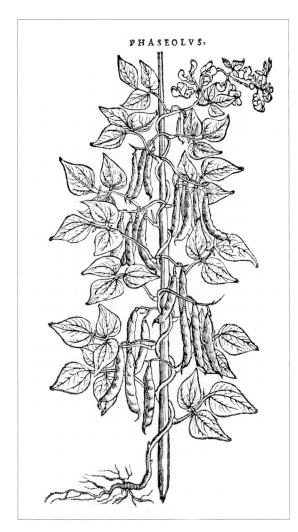

PHASEOLUS, woodcut. Rembert Dodoens,
*Historium Frumentorum, Leguminum,
Palustrium et Aquatilium Herbarum*, 1569.
(CMLA).

Fuchs's herbal. The later botanical works of
Dodoens were printed by the celebrated Plantin
publishing house which dominated the field of
botanical printing during the latter half of the
sixteenth century.

The University of Montpellier played an
important role in the development of the other
botanical writers associated with Plantin's press.
It was there that Pierre Pena, Matthias de
L'Obel, and Clusius came as medical students
and studied under the renowned zoologist, ich-
thyologist, and botanist, Guillaume Rondelet.

The *Stirpium Adversaria Nova* of Pena and
L'Obel and its reissue by Plantin as a companion volume to L'Obel's *Plantarum seu Stirpium
Adversaria* under the title of *Nova Stirpium
Adversaria* have already been discussed in the
preceding chapter. The works are of particular
interest in the development of classification
systems since they grouped plants according
to whether they had monocotyledonous or dicotyledonous leaves.

The main botanical author, editor, and
translator associated with the Plantin publishing house, however, was Clusius. Although
Clusius enjoyed a multi-faceted career as a lawyer, physician, botanist, editor, and translator,
he is best remembered for his botanical work.
He is first encountered in the Cleveland collections through his 1557 French translation
of Dodoens's *Cruydeboeck* as *Histoire des Plantes*,
which we have already mentioned. This was accompanied by a second French translation by
Clusius apparently derived from an unspeci-
fied German herbal and published under the
title *Petit Recueil, auquel Est Contenue la Description d'Aucunes Gommes et Liqueurs, Provenans Tant
des Arbres, que des Herbes*. He is next encountered through the series of abridged Latin translations of the works of Monardes, da Orta, and
Acosta that Clusius created for Plantin during
the 1560's and 1570's, which we have already
discussed in the previous chapter.

Clusius's first original book was the
*Rariorum aliquot Stirpium per Hispanias
Observatarum Historia* published by Plantin in
1576. The work recorded the author's botanical observations on plants encountered on a
botanizing expedition, which he had undertaken
to Spain and Portugal in 1564 and 1565, along
with some observations which he had made as
a student at Montpellier.

In his *Rariorum aliquot Stirpium per
Pannonium [et] Austriam Observatarum Historia*,
first published in 1583 and 1584, Clusius established the first floras for Hungary and Aus-

tria. The work proved somewhat problematical with errors that forced him to have Plantin replace and cancel some sections. This resulted in two distinct issues of the work that are both present in the Cleveland collections. Cleveland also has the 1584 Plantin edition of his *Stirpium Nomenclator Pannonicus.* The only known copy of the first edition, printed by a different press in 1583, is believed to have been destroyed.

Clusius went on to lead a distinguished career in which he served as director of the Imperial Gardens in Vienna from 1573 to 1587, and later succeeded his friend Dodoens as professor of botany at Leyden in 1593, where he also founded the botanical garden. His botanical writings were collected in two volumes for the Plantin Press which issued the first volume, the *Rariorum Plantarum Historia*, in 1601. This volume included the first publication of Clusius's *Fungorum Historia*, one of the first published monographs on fungi. The second volume, entitled *Exoticarum Libri Decem*, was published in 1605.

A final note on the sixteenth century concerns a pupil of Rondelet at Montpellier. Jacques Dalechamps, a French physician and botanist, compiled a massive botanical work entitled *Historia Generalis Plantarum* that was published at Lyons in 1586 and 1587. Unfortunately, since Dalechamps was largely preoccupied with his medical practice, the editing of the work was placed in the hands of Jean Bauhin and left to be completed by Jean Desmoulins, who inadvertently left Dalechamps's name off the title page.

THE SEVENTEENTH century was marked by increased efforts at systematizing and classifying plants and a new interest in exploring plant physiology with the aid of the microscope. Some works were more philosophical in nature, and while appearing to be based upon scientific experiments, they presented results and conclusions that could not be readily duplicated. A prime example of the latter is the essay *Of the Vegetation of Plants* written by the English Catholic philosopher, adventurer, and courtier, Sir Kenelm Digby. The paper, which was originally delivered to the Royal Society in 1661, is represented in Cleveland by the third English and fourth overall edition published in 1669 as part of the collection entitled *Of Bodies, and of Man's Soul . . . with Two Discourses of the Powder of Sympathy, and of the Vegetation of Plants*. The work discusses the germination, nutrition, and growth of plants. It then goes on, however, to describe a series of experiments in which Digby claimed to be able to revivify plants that were frozen or burnt to ashes.

Guy de la Brosse, the French botanist and chemist, who was physician in ordinary to Louis XIII of France and the founder and first director of the Jardin des Plantes, discussed items such as the nature of the souls of plants, the sensitivity of plants, and varieties in species of plants in his *De la Nature, Vertu, et Utilité des Plantes* (1628). In the same work, de la Brosse also deduced that air was needed to nourish plants, although he did so on the wrong evidence.

The seventeenth century microscopists represented in the Cleveland collections are Robert Hooke, Nehemiah Grew, Marcello Malpighi, and Antony von Leeuwenhoek. The earliest of their works in the Cleveland collections is the first edition, first issue of Hooke's *Micrographia* published in 1665.

Hooke was an English scientist, inventor, surveyor, architect, and professor of geometry at Gresham College in London. He was also at various times the curator, librarian, and secretary of the Royal Society of London. His work, which also includes telescopic observations, is generally regarded as the first book to present significant microscopic observations on plant anatomy. Among the items discussed and examined are leaf mold, sea weed, leaf surfaces, the stinging portions of nettles, and petrified wood. From a biological point of view, it is important for Hooke's discussion of the examination of the structure of cork, in the course of which he coined the term "cell" as used in modern biology.

Co-founders of the science of plant anatomy include Marcello Malpighi, an Italian physician, anatomist, philosopher, and botanist who served at various times as professor of medicine at the Universities of Bologna and Messina, and Nehemiah Grew, an English physician and botanist. Malpighi is represented in the collections by the first edition of his *Opera Omnia* (1686), while Grew is represented by the first edition of his *The Anatomy of Plants* (1682).

Probably the best known of the microscopists was Antony van Leeuwenhoek. A Dutch self-taught scientist who started as a shopkeeper in the cloth trade, he spent most of his career as a civil servant for the city of Delft. Ignorant of foreign languages, he came to the attention of the scientific community primarily through translations of his Dutch correspondence with the Royal Society. Leeuwenhoek's research centered on sexual reproduction and on the transport system of nutrients in both plants and animals.

The rare book collection of the Cleveland Medical Library Association contains several printed collections of Leeuwenhoek's letters in

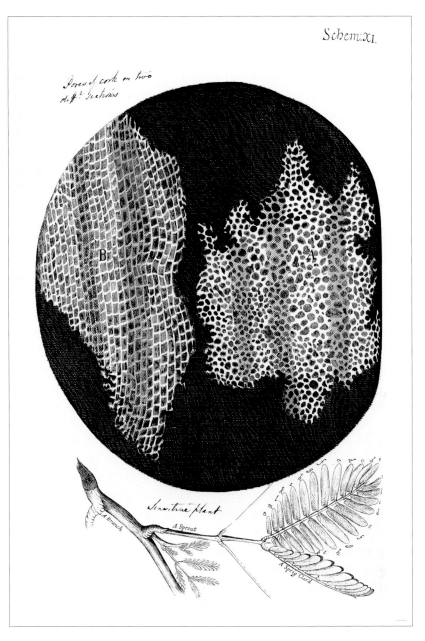

MICROSCOPIC VIEWS OF CORK and **ILLUSTRATION OF A SENSITIVE PLANT**, engraving. Robert Hooke, *Micrographia*, 1665. (CMLA).

their original Dutch versions. In the first edition of the letters headed *Ontledingen en ontdekkingen van het Begin der Planten in de Zaden van Boomen* published in 1685, Leeuwenhoek discusses the structure of tree seeds, embryos in various plants, the existence of male and female trees, and his theory of the intercellular transfer of nutrients. The first edition of the letters, headed *Ontledingen en ontdekkingen van de Cinnaber Naturalis* and published in 1686, contains further descriptions of seeds and embryos, a discussion of galls and secretions in plants, and a comparison of the wood of oak and pine coupled with a discussion of their rings in relation to the seasons. The second edition of the *Vervolg der Brieven* published in 1688, although not mainly botanical in subject matter, does contain discussions of coffee, cinchona bark, and observations on the beginnings of roots in barley.

The Cleveland collections also include *Epistolae Physiologicae Super Compluribus Naturae Arcanis* published in 1719, the first edition of the Latin translation of Leeuwenhoek letters written between 1712 and 1717; and a copy of Samuel Hoole's English translation of Leeuwenhoek's *Select Works* that contains both halves of part one and the first half of part two (published in 1798 and 1799), but lacks the 1800 second half of part two and part three published in 1807.

The collections also contain the works of two later German botanical microscopists. Martin Frobenius Ledermüller, a lawyer with a penchant for botany and microscopy, was a protegé of Christoph Jakob Trew, who was a Nuremberg physician and the patron of numerous botanical artists, writers, and publications. Ledermüller is represented in Cleveland by his uncompleted *Mikroscopische Gemüths und Augen-Ergötzung* published from 1760 to about 1783, and by his *Versuch, beÿ angehender Frühlings Zeit die Vergröszerungs Werckzeuge ... anzuwensen* published in 1764.

The other German represented in this area is Wilhelm Friedrich Gleichen-Russworm, a soldier, who after retiring from the military to manage his familial estates, spent much of his leisure time in experimenting with the microscope. He is represented in Cleveland by his *Decouvertes les Plus Nouvelles dans le Regne Vegetal*, a French translation published in 1770 of a work originally published in German from 1763 to 1766. It includes microscopic views of pollen and fertilization.

The seventeenth century saw numerous attempts to develop a taxonomy, or system of classification, based upon natural characteristics, for plants, as well as for the other kingdoms of nature. Most of these systems are considered, like the 18th century system of Linnaeus, to be *artificial* rather than *natural* since they tend to group plants based on a single characteristic aspect or organ rather than on the basis of the whole plant.

A seminal work in taxonomy was the *Pinax, Theatrum Botanici* of Gaspard Bauhin published in 1623. Bauhin was a Swiss anatomist, botanist, chemist, and physician who occupied several posts in the course of his career at the University of Basel. The work is of major importance as the first work to clearly make the differentiation between genus and species and to use this to establish a Latin binomial system of naming plants. It also attempted to bring order to the mass of names which had accrued to various plants over the years by including a complete synonomy for each plant based on all the authors to whom he had access.

Robert Morison was a Scottish physician and botanist who led a colorful life. A Royalist in the time of Oliver Cromwell, he fled to France where he was appointed along with Abel Brunyer and Nicolas Marchant by Duke Gaston of Orleans to head the operation of the royal garden at Blois. After the Restoration, he returned to England where he was given the appointments of King's Physician and Regius Professor of Botany under Charles II. In 1672, his *Plantarum Umbelliferarum* was published. This has been cited by Sachs as "the first monograph which was intended to carry out systematic principles strictly within the limits of a single large family."

Morison's other major publication consisted of the second and third parts of his *Plantarum Historiae Universalis Oxoniensis* (1680

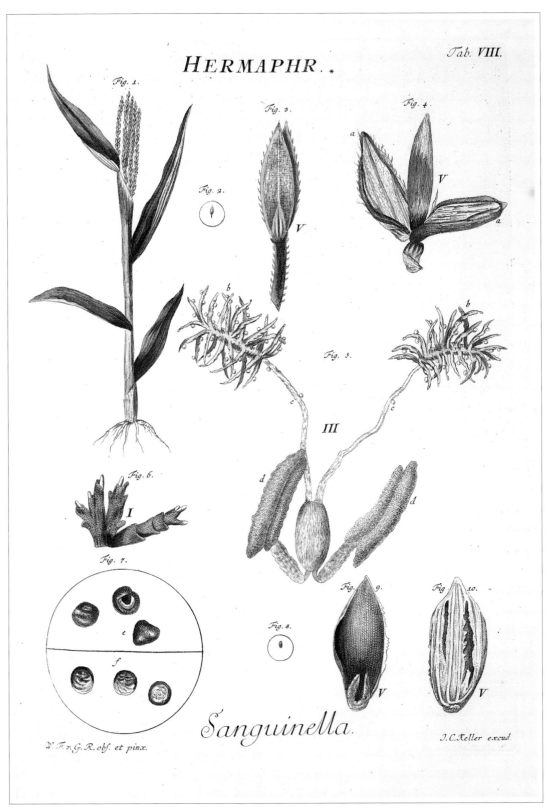

SANGUINELLA engraved by J. C. Keller after W. F. Gleichen-Russworm. Wilhelm Friedrich Gleichen-Russworm, *Decouvertes les Plus Nouvelles dans le Regne Vegetal*, 1770. (GC).

and 1699), with the third part completed after Morison's death by Jacob Bobart the younger. Bobart had succeeded his father to become the second keeper of the Oxford physic garden. The work attempted to classify all known plants, but the first part, that was to have dealt with trees and shrubs, was never published, and may never have been written.

Morison employed an artificial system of classification based on the characters exhibited by the fruit and seed. In contrast, Augustus Quirinus Bachmann, better known as Rivinus, established a system of classification which placed the emphasis on the flower. Rivinus, a German physician who served at various times as professor of botany and physiology, and of pathology, at the University of Leipzig, began publication of his theory with the *Introductio Generalis in Rem Herbariam* in 1690. This was succeeded by his *Ordo Plantarum, Quae Sunt Flore Irregulari Monopetalo* in the same year, his *Ordo Plantarum, Quae Sunt Flore Irregulari Tetrapetalo* in 1691, and his *Ordo Plantarum, Quae Sunt Flore Irregulari Pentapetalo* in 1699. The works classified plants according to the number and the symmetry of their petals and advocated a binomial system of nomenclature.

Joseph Pitton de Tournefort also developed a system of classification, based primarily on the form of the corolla. Tournefort was a French botanist and physician who trained at Aix and Montpellier and became professor of botany at the Jardin des Plantes. Tournefort's system divided flowering plants into the large categories of trees and herbs. Each of these categories was then divided into groups based on whether their flowers were petal-bearing or nonpetal-bearing, simple or compound, and regular or irregular, with subclasses depending on the superior or inferior position of the ovary. As shown in Franz Balthasar Lindern's *Tournefortius Alsaticus* published in 1728, the system prevailed in western Europe until displaced by the Linnaean system and continued

to dominate French botany until superceded by the system of Jussieu. The latter was initially introduced in the *Elemens de Botanique* (1694). More importantly, Tournefort used the work to develop the concept of the genus as the smallest practical unit of classification. He considered the species as variants of the genus, thus laying the groundwork for the use of genus in the modern sense.

The great British naturalist John Ray, although a contemporary of Morison, Rivinus, and Tournefort, took a radically different approach to his botanical classification. Beginning with the distinction between monocotyledonous and dicotyledonous plants, with classes based on fruit type, and further subdivisions based on leaf and flower forms, Ray gradually developed what many consider to be the first of the natural systems of botanical classification.

Ray is first represented in the Cleveland collections by his earliest book on scientific botany, the *Catalogus Plantarum circa Cantabrigiam Nascentium* of 1660. The Cleveland copy has both the corrected title page and the uncorrected title page. The uncorrected title page was normally cancelled and would not appear in the published volume.

The next work present is the *Historia Plantarum* published in three volumes from 1686 through 1704. The book is generally regarded as the first attempt at a world flora. The first volume is particularly noteworthy for its initial section that summarizes all that was known about botany to that time. Ray's detailed descriptions of the plants were not accompanied by illustrations because of the cost, but this lack was partially compensated for through the publication of 50 plates depicting 501 plants engraved by Nicholas Sutton and published in 1713 as *A Catalogue of Mr. Ray's English Herbal Illustrated with Figures on Folio Copper Plates* (an additional 12 plates were published in 1715, but are not present in the Cleveland collections). The publication of the plates was arranged by James Petiver, an English apothecary who had assisted Ray with several of his books.

The development of Ray's system of classification is reflected in the *Variis Plantarum Methodis Dissertatio Brevis* of 1696 in which he replies to Tournefort's criticisms of it. Also in the collections is the second edition of Ray's *Synopsis Methodica Stirpium Britannicarum*, the last edition of this handbook of the British species published during Ray's life. It is considerably expanded from the original edition of 1690, and it is accompanied by Rivinus's *Epistola ad Joan. Raium* also published in 1696. This latter work features Rivinus's attacks on Ray's system and Ray's response.

*T*HE BEGINNING of the eighteenth century witnessed the rise of experimental science. The most noted botanical experimentalist of the early portion of the century was Stephen Hales, the English cleric whose observations revolutionized the studies of botanical and human physiology.

By a series of ingenious experiments on plants, Hales built upon the observations made earlier by Malpighi and Grew and established the movement of sap in plants, and the need for air in the growth of the plant. Hales measured root suction, root pressure, and leaf suction, and demonstrated and studied transpiration in the leaves. The results of his experiments were first published as *Vegetable Staticks* in 1727 and were later combined with his experiments on animal physiology to form a set issued under the combined title of *Statical Essays* beginning in 1733. The popularity of the work is evidenced by numerous English and foreign editions. The latter are represented in

Cleveland by *Statica de Vegetabili ed Analisi dell'Aria*, the Italian version of 1776.

Not all experimental work was so successful, however, as witnessed by the case of Charles Bonnet's *Recherches Sur l'Usage des Feuilles dans les Plantes* (1754). Bonnet was a Swiss lawyer and philosopher who distinguished himself in his entomological research to such an extent that he is often regarded as one of the fathers of modern biology. The experiments with plants detailed in this work, however, were ill-conceived and of no value since they were conducted with dead leaves. His ideas impeded the progress of

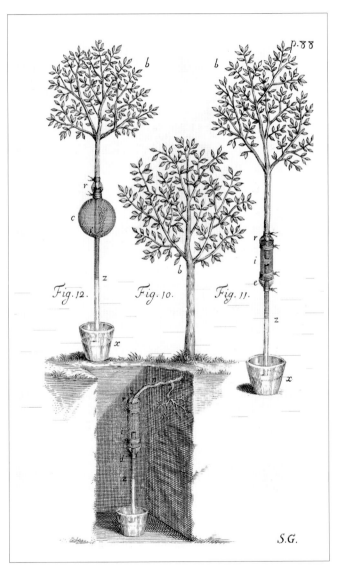

ENGRAVING by Simon Gribelin illustrative of some of Hales' experiments. Stephen Hales, *Vegetable Staticks*, 1727. (CMLA).

research in plant physiology by those who, placing credence in Bonnet's reputation, chose to believe his conclusions that a chief function of the leaves was to absorb the dew rising from the ground.

One of the people to adopt this view was Henri Louis Duhamel du Monceau, the great French writer on trees, who made it part of his *Physique des Arbres* of 1758. In other respects, Duhamel's work on the physiology of trees is more perceptive and is based on the observations of Malpighi and Hales as well as his own experiments. The book also includes a dissertation on the various botanical systems of classification, including a detailed account of that of Tournefort, and a useful dictionary of French botanical and agricultural terms.

In the early eighteenth century, there was a continuation of the influx of new plants not only from the Americas, but from the Orient as well.

The year 1714 saw the publication of the first part of a specialized flora of the Pacific coast of Chile and Peru in a work bearing the lengthy title *Journal des Observations Physiques, Mathematiques et Botaniques Faites par l'Ordre du Roy Sur les Côtes Orientales de l'Amerique Meridionale, & dans les Indes Occidentales, depuis l'Année 1707, jusques en 1712.* It is by the French Franciscan astronomer, mathematician, and botanist, Louis Feuillée. Although the primary purpose of the expedition was to determine exact longtitudes, Feuillée managed to record some fifty specimens of plants.

Information on Japanese plants is likewise submerged in a larger work entitled *Amoenitatum Exoticarum Politico-Physico-Medicarum Fasciculi V* published in 1712 and composed by Engelbert Kaempfer. Kaempfer was a German naturalist, botanist, and physician whose career included accompanying a Swedish embassy to Russia and Persia, serving as a surgeon with the Dutch East India Company in Java and Japan, and serving as personal physician to the Count of Lippe. This account draws on his various travels and experiences. It includes his prodromus for a full-sized Japanese flora that was never published and the earliest plate of a camellia, which was published under its Japanese name of *tsubaki*.

THE CONTINUING deluge of new and exotic flora that bombarded the European botanists created the need for a system of classification that could be easily applied and that would simplify the task of discussing the new plants. This paved the way for the most celebrated of the artifical systems, the sexual system created by Carl Linnaeus.

The earliest work by Linnaeus in the Cleveland collections is the *Musa Cliffortiana* (1736). The work was written during Linnaeus's visit to Holland during that period when he was serving as personal physician and supervisor of gardens at the Hartecamp estate of George Clifford, the wealthy Anglo-Dutch banker and director of the East India Company. The work commemorates Linnaeus's successful induction of a blossom on Clifford's banana tree through a detailed account of the plant and the circumstances that led it to blossom. The Cleveland copy has extra associational interest since it once belonged to Minor C. Keith, who has been credited with planting the first banana tree in Costa Rica.

Linnaeus's relationship with Clifford also led to the publication of the *Hortus Cliffortianus* commemorating the rare and exotic plants grown in Clifford's gardens and hothouse. The work is easily the most beautiful of Linnaeus's publications with full descriptions of the plants and lavish full page plates of the plants engraved by Jan Wandelaar after the original illustrations by Georg Dionysius Ehret. It bears a publica-

TURNERA A PETIOLO FLORENS, FOLIIS FERRATIS,
engraving by Jan Wandelaar after Georg
Dionysius Ehret. Carl Linnaeus, *Hortus
Cliffortiana*, 1737 [-1738]. (GC).

tions. Thus the **Fundamenta Botanica** first published in 1730, which contains the basic philosophy of Linnaeus's botanical thought in the form of a series of aphorisms, is first found in Cleveland in a 1744 Parisian reprint of the second edition. Its revision as the **Philosophia Botanica** is found in an 1824 edition. The **Bibliotheca Botanica**, Linnaeus's bibliography of previous botanical writers, is here in the second edition of 1747. The **Genera Plantarum**, originally published in 1737, is represented by a Parisian edition of 1743 (which adds French vernacular plant names), by the Swedish imprints of 1754 (which is considered of nomenclatural significance today) and 1764 (the last edition published during Linnaeus's lifetime), and the Strassburg imprint of 1789 to 1791. Unlike most of the botanical works, the **Species Plantarum** is present in the first edition of 1753. This edition is considered to have established the binomial system of nomenclature and is regarded by many as the most important work in botanical literature and the starting point of modern taxonomy. The **Species Plantarum** is also represented by the expanded version published in 1762 and 1763. It contains Linnaeus's main body of discussion on the use of binomials and

tion date of 1737 but was only made available to Clifford's friends in 1738 and was not available to the general public until 1739.

Linnaeus's **Flora Lapponica** was published in 1737 and served as the first publication in monographic form of the botanical fruits of his 1732 expedition to Lapland. Also dating from this period is Linnaeus's edition of his friend Petrus Artedi's **Ichthyologia**. This work on fishes was published in 1738, following Artedi's unfortunate death by drowning and Clifford's successful attempt, at Linnaeus's instigation, to retrieve Artedi's manuscript from the author's landlord, who held it in lieu of past due rent.

Most of the early botanical works that served to establish Linnaeus's reputation are represented in Cleveland by relatively late edi-

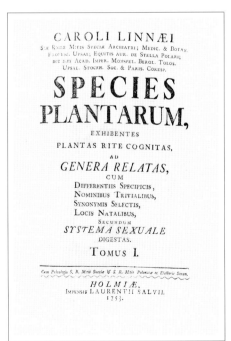

TITLE PAGE. Carl Linnaeus, **Species Plantarum**, 1753. (GC).

was the standard edition used by the eighteenth and nineteenth century botanists.

Other Linnaean botanical works in the collections include the first edition of the *Flora Zeylanica* published in 1747 and the first edition of the *Hortus Upsaliensis*, Linnnaeus's catalogue of the Uppsala botanic garden published in 1748.

Linnaeus's *Systema Naturae* was an attempt to systematize animals and minerals, as well as plants. It is represented by the fourth edition of 1744, and is also present in the tenth edition of 1758 to 1759 and the twelfth edition of 1766 to 1768. The tenth edition was the first to apply the binomial system to the other natural kingdoms, with the exception of minerals since the mineral section was never printed. The twelfth edition includes the *Mantissa Plantarum,* which supplements the genera given by Linnaeus in the *Genera Plantarum.*

Among the many other non-botanical works by Linnaeus included in the collections are the first edition of the *Fauna Svecica* published in 1746, the *Museum Alpho-Fridericianum* published in 1746, and the *Museum Tessinianum* published in 1753.

Botanical and medical theses, often written by Linnaeus, but defended by his students, are present in a mixed collection of the *Amoenitates Academicae* published from 1749 through 1790, as well as in some individual monographs. Linnaeus's lectures are represented by the *Praelectiones in Ordines Naturales Plantarum* published in 1792 and edited by Paul Dieterich Giseke, a German physician and botanist who had studied under Linnaeus. Linnaeus's correspondence and personal papers are reflected in the 1805 second edition of Richard Pulteney's *A General View of the Writings of Linnaeus* and in the 1821 first edition of *A Selection of the Correspondence of Linnaeus and the Other Naturalists* edited by J. E. Smith. The former includes William G. Maton's memoirs of

Linnaeus and C. Troilius's translation of Linnaeus's diary.

The Linnaean system of botanical classification grouped plants into 24 classes according to the number of stamens and their relative order and then divided the classes according to the number of pistils. It came to be widely accepted throughout Europe and was especially dominant in Holland, Germany, and England. In France, however, although the Linnaean system was introduced as early as 1749 in Thomas François Dalibard's *Florae Parisiensis Prodromus*, many botanical writers either continued using Tournefort's system or were moving toward the development of a natural system of classification. Preeminent among the French botanists working to develop a natural system were members of the Jussieu family. Bernard de Jussieu, who succeeded Vaillant as botanical demonstrator at the Jardin du Roi, was given the task of arranging a new botanical garden on the grounds of the Petit Trianon at Versailles. In doing so, he arranged the plants in a natural order. Although Bernard never published anything relating to his natural system, the garden itself set an example for botanists until its destruction from 1774 to 1777 to make way for an English park more to the taste of Marie-Antoinette. One of those who noted the example set by Bernard de Jussieu was Louis Gerard, a French provincial physician and botanist, who has been credited with publishing the first flora arranged according to a natural system of classification in his *Flora Galloprovincialis* of 1761. While this work follows the system of Bernard, it also contains a number of departures from it that were Gerard's own innovations.

Bernard de Jussieu's natural arrangement also was used to organize the material within each section of Antoine-Nicolas Duchesne's *Manuel de Botanique* (1764). The author, a French botanist and professor of natural history at École Centrale de Sein-et-Oise and the

Lycée de Versailles, was also connected with the Trianon botanic garden where he learned about the system from Bernard. The system is not explained, however, but only used to organize the discussion of the economic uses of the plants within each section of the work.

It was left to one of Bernard de Jussieu's pupils, Michel Adanson, to initially analyze and explain the foundations of natural classification and define the practical method to be used in seeking such a system. Adanson attended classes at both the Collège Royale and the Jardin du Roi where he studied under Bernard, among others. He then spent several years in Senegal as an employee of the Compagnie des Indes, during which time he botanized extensively and studied the natural history of the area. It was there, amid the wealth of strange and exotic flora, that Adanson became convinced that none of the then current systems could adequately handle this new material. On his return to France, he lived with Bernard de Jussieu for the next ten years during which he devised his own natural system of classification. The work, published as the **Familles des Plantes** in 1763, advocated examining the totality of each plant from root to embryo, rather than any one isolated feature, and then comparing this with the totality of other plants to establish families based on multiple similarities. He then went on to establish a series of families based upon his observations, established the relationships between these families, and in turn examined the relationships between the different genera within each family. In the course of his investigations, he also introduced the concept of mutability of species. Unfortunately, although the **Familles** was widely and favorably reviewed upon its publication, Adanson fell into a state of disrepute owing partially to his insistence on his own eccentric personal spelling, his failure to capitalize on the **Familles** with successive publications expanding on it, and his stubborn rejection of the Linnaean concept of

binomial names that had become universally accepted.

Jean Pierre Bergeret, the French surgeon whose patients included the brother of King Louis XVI (later Louis XVIII), devised what may best be described as an artificial natural system for the classification and naming of plants. In his scheme, Bergeret set up a series of 15 tables, each dealing with a different physical aspect of the plant, such as the corolla. He then assigned a different letter to each possible variation of that aspect, with the letter A always used for an element not present (and a superscript number following the A to indicate a succession of aspects that are not present). The letters were then to be written in the order of the tables to produce the "universal name" of the plant, such as A^8LA^4YZ for the plant classified by Linnaeus as *Agaricus muscarius*. The work, which appears to have been published from 1783 through 1786 as **Phytonomatotechnie Universelle**, accompanied each name with detailed descriptions of the plant and citations of its place in the systems of Tournefort, Linnaeus, and Jussieu. Unfortunately, the Cleveland copy has only the first of the fifteen tables.

It was left to Bernard de Jussieu's nephew, Antoine-Laurent de Jussieu, to expand on Adanson's basic principles and popularize the natural system through the publication of the **Genera Plantarum Secundum Ordines Naturales Disposita** in 1789, the same year as the French revolution. Antoine-Laurent de Jussieu was a French botanist and physician who had served as deputy to L. G. Le Monnier, when he was professor of botany at the Jardin du Roi. He also served at one time as physician to King Louis XVI. After the revolution, he became professor of botany at the Muséum National d'Histoire Naturelle and eventually its director. This work, which built on the Adansonian system of multi-affinities, but which retained the almost universally used Linnaean system

Primula veris, rubro flore. I.R.H.124. — Primula veris, flore sanguineo, simplici, umbilico croceo. Cat.H.R. — Ital. Fiori di Primavera. — Gall. Primever...

PRIMULO VERIS, RUBRO FLORE engraved by Magdalen Bouchard after Cesare Ubertini. Giorgio Bonelli and Niccolo Martelli, ***Hortus Romanus***, 1772-1793. (HA).

of nomenclature, served as the basis of the later natural systems.

Although inroads were made with the development of a natural system, much of the botanical work throughout most of the eighteenth century either remained based on Linnaeus's system or was done in reaction to it. Thus, Albrecht von Haller, the Swiss physician, botanist, and civil servant, devised his own artifical system for use in his *Historia Stirpium Indigenarum Helvetiae* (1768) because he felt that Linnaeus's system was too simple. The *Hortus Romanus,* published from 1772 through 1793, had the first volume arranged in Tournefortian order by Giorgio Bonelli, while the subsequent seven volumes arranged by Niccolo Martelli also followed Tournefortian order, but added the Linnaean binomials for the plants.

On a more exotic level, 1768 saw the publication of the *Flora Indica* and *Prodromus Florae Capensis,* which Frans Stafleu[1] regards as the first general tropical flora in the Linnaean style. The work is a list and descriptions of the plants of India, Java, and Ceylon, supplemented by appendices on the zoophytes of India and on the flora of the Cape of Good Hope. It was written by Nicolas Laurens Burmann, who succeeded his father, Jan Burmann, as professor of botany at Amsterdam.

A number of works in the Cleveland collections were written by former students of Linnaeus, who after their graduation accompanied various groups on voyages of exploration and discovery. Perhaps the most notable of these is Carl Peter Thunberg, a Swedish botanist and physician, who joined the Dutch East India Company as a surgeon and subsequently spent three years at the Cape of Good Hope, where, among other things, he practiced his Dutch. This was the prelude to his journey to Japan, where he passed himself off as a Dutch national since these were the only Europeans allowed to land there. In Japan, he was restricted in his

movements, but managed to assemble a significant collection of botanical specimens from young Japanese who brought the specimens in exchange for Thunberg's instruction in Western medicine. The fruits of his trip to Japan were published in 1784 as the *Flora Japonica*. Eventually Thunberg succeeded the younger Linnaeus as professor of botany in the medical school at Uppsala.

SALVIA JAPONICA, engraving by S. N. Caström. Carl Peter Thunberg, *Flora Japonica*, 1784. (GC).

The Linnaean school of classification was especially strong in England from about 1760. It received an added impetus in 1784 when James Edward Smith, who was at that time a medical student, purchased Linnaeus's collections, correspondence, and library from the estate of the younger Linnaeus. After completing his medical studies, Smith devoted much

[1]Frans Stafleu is a leading expert in botanical taxonomy. Reference is to: Stafleu, Frans A., and Cowan, Richard S. *Taxonomic Literature,* 2nd ed. 7 vol. Utrecht/Antwerp: Bohn, Scheltema, & Holkema; The Hague/Boston: dr. W Junk b. v., Publishers, 1976-1988.

of the rest of his life to botany. In 1788, Smith, together with The Rev. Samuel Goodenough and Thomas Marsham, founded the Linnean Society, which Smith was to serve as president of for the remainder of his life. This group, which purchased the Linnean collections after Smith's death and continues to preserve them to the present day, is represented in Cleveland by the first eight volumes of its published *Transactions* (1791 through 1807).

Smith is represented in the collections by his earliest botanical work, the English translation of Linnaeus's *A Dissertation on the Sexes of Plants* published in 1786. In the introduction, Smith takes note of the attacks on the system by Adanson and by the Abbé Lazzaro Spallanzani. This latter attack originally appeared in Italian in 1784 as the *Dissertazioni di Fisica Animale e Vegetabile*, and is represented in Cleveland by the first English translation, *Dissertations Relative to the Natural History of Animals and Vegetables* (1789).

Smith is also represented by his *Syllabus of a Course of Lectures on Botany* that covers plant physiology and the Linnaean system and was published for the benefit of the staff of St. Guy's Hospital in 1795, by a second edition (1809) of one his most popular works, *An Introduction to Physiological and Systematical Botany*, and by the first edition of his final work, *The English Flora* published from 1824 to 1828.

As we have noted, however, the interest in Linnaeus by the British botanical community was not confined to Smith and the Linnean Society. The earliest English translation of one of Linnaeus's works was the *Philosophia Botanica* translated by the gardener and nurseryman James Lee. It was first published as *An Introduction to Botany* in 1760, and is represented in Cleveland by the fifth edition of 1794.

In 1764, the Englishman John Berkenhout, who would go on to become a physician, naturalist, and writer of miscellaneous works, pub-

lished his *Clavis Anglicae Linguae Botanicae*, a dictionary of botanical terms as used in the Linnaean system. Berkenhout composed this work while a medical student at Edinburgh at the request of and under the supervision of John Hope, professor of medicine. In addition to the original edition, Cleveland also has a copy of a portion of pirated text that was published in *The Pomona Britanica* of 1788.

In 1776, the English physician, botanist, chemist, mineralogist, climatologist, inventor, and dog and cattle breeder, William Withering, published his *A Botanical Arrangement of All the Vegetables Naturally Growing in Great Britain*. It is both the first outstanding work on English plants to be published in English and the first flora of Great Britain to use the Linnaean binomial system of nomenclature.

Withering numbered among his circle of friends Erasmus Darwin, the English physician of Lichfield and grandfather of Charles Darwin. Darwin was also interested in the works of Linnaeus, and he along with Brooke Boothby and John Jackson formed the Lichfield Botanical Society. The Society produced the first English translations of Linnaeus's *Systema Vegetabilium (A System of Vegetables,* 1782 through 1785 but with a title date of 1783), and his *Genera Plantarum (The Families of Plants,* 1787). The latter was based on the seventh edition of 1778, with additional material from the *Mantissae Plantarum* editions of 1767 and 1771, and the *Supplementum Plantarum Systematis Vegetabilium* of the younger Linnaeus published in 1781.

Linnaeus was also the source for the second part of Darwin's celebrated botanical poem *The Botanic Garden*, called *The Loves of the Plants* and based on Linnaeus's sexual system. It was no accident that this second and more sensational section was published first in 1789, while the first part entitled *The Economy of Vegetation* did not appear until 1791. The earliest copy in the Cleveland collections dates from 1791 and joins the first edition of the first part with the third edition of the second part. Also in Cleveland is the 1800 first edition of Darwin's *Phytologia*.

Although Linnaeus's influence waned in England in the nineteenth century, it is not insignificant to note the publication of Richard Duppa's *The Classes and Orders of the Linnaean System of Botany* (1816).

Spanish botany is represented in the Cleveland collections by two works by Antonio José Cavanilles, the Spanish botanist who studied under Antoine-Laurent de Jussieu and J. B. P. A. de M. de Lamarck while serving as preceptor to the children of the Duke of Infantado when the latter was Spanish Ambassador to France. He later was made professor of botany and director of the botanical garden at Madrid. The *Monadelphiae Classis Dissertationes Decem* of 1785 to 1790 constitutes Cavanilles's earliest botanical publication. In it, he describes 712 plants using the Linnaean system. His *Icones et Descriptiones Plantarum, Quae aut Sponte in Hispania Crescunt* is a flora of Spain published from 1791 through 1801.

Portuguese botany is also represented in the collections by Felix Avellar Brotero's *Compendio de Botanica* published in 1788, *Phytographia Lusitania Selectior* published from 1816 to 1827, and the *Diccionario dos Termos Technicos de Historia Natural* published in 1788 by Domenico Vandelli. Vandelli was an Italian physician, botanist, and chemist, who served as professor of botany and chemistry at the University of Coimbra, where he also founded the botanical garden.

*T*URNING TOWARD North America, we should probably begin with the *Canadensium Plantarum Historia,* published in 1635, which is usually considered the first Canadian flora. The work was compiled by Jacques Cornut, a French physician who, although he never traveled to the New World, had connections with the French explorers who provided seeds and specimens of North American plants that he used in his garden.

The Cleveland collections feature a number of eighteenth century accounts of North American plants. One of these is the second edition of Johan Frederic Gronovius's *Flora Virginica* published in 1762 and based upon specimens supplied by John Clayton, the son of the attorney-general of Virginia. Another is the first issue of the first edition of the *Hortus Britanno-Americanus* that Mark Catesby published in 1763. The Cleveland copy has the title-page of its second issue as the *Hortus Europae Americanae* of 1767 laid-in as a loose leaf. The plates of this latter work are redrawn and condensed from those in Catesby's *The Natural History of Carolina, Florida, and the Bahama Islands*, that was originally published from 1731 to 1743 (but present in the Cleveland collections only in the third edition of 1771). The descriptions are largely verbatim from *The Natural History*, but with additions for adapting American trees and shrubs to England.

The next noteworthy catalogue of North American plants in the collections is the *Flora Americae Septentrionalis* of Johann Reinhold Forster published in 1771. The author was a German traveler and naturalist of English descent, who was a preacher in Danzig and Russia before settling in England where he taught French, German, and natural history at the Warrington Academy and served as a translator. This catalogue of all known North American plants contained their English and Linnaean names, the places they were found, and references to earlier literature concerning them. Subsequent to its writing, Forster was appointed naturalist to Captain Cook's Pacific expedition of 1772 to 1775, served a term in debtor's prison partially as a result of a dispute with the Admiralty, and finally returned to Germany where he became professor of natural history at the University of Halle.

The first indigenous botanical essay to be published in the western hemisphere is generally considered to be Humphry Marshall's *Arbustrum Americanum* published in Philadelphia in 1785. The author was a Pennsylvania farmer and one-time stonemason whose interest in botany and agriculture led him to build one of the first conservatories in the American colonies (circa 1768) as well as a botanical garden. The work is entirely devoted to listing American shrubs and trees.

We have already observed in the work by Forster, the implicit English interest in importing American shrubs and trees for both ornamental and economic purposes. The French had a similar interest in North American forests which led the French government to send a special delegation composed of André Michaux, his son, François André Michaux, and the journeyman gardener, Paul Saulnier, to the United States in 1785 to study the North American trees with an eye towards possible introduction of species to France and their utility for naval construction.

André Michaux was born into a line of royal estate managers. Prior to this mission and following the death of this wife, he had studied botany with Le Monnier and Bernard de Jussieu, botanized in England, the Auvergne, and the Pyrenees, and spent a brief period as secretary to the French consul in Persia. He left this post to spend three years botanizing in Asia Minor. In the United States, Michaux and his companions botanized from Hudson's Bay to Florida and from the East Coast to the Midwest, collecting specimens along the way which they brought back to form the initial stock of nurseries they set up in Hackensack, New Jersey, and Charleston, South Carolina.

In 1796, virtually out of funds, the Michauxs returned to France, but they failed to gain funding for the continuation of the American mission. While seeking the funding, André Michaux composed his classic work on American oaks, *Histoire des Chênes de l'Amérique*. The work was left for his son, François André, to see through the press, however, as André joined Captain Nicolas Baudin's expedition to Australia in 1800. Unfortunately, André Michaux never reached Australia. After setting up a botanical garden in Mauritius, he left the expedition to botanize in Madagascar, where he soon died.

The *Histoire des Chênes* finally appeared under François André's editorship in 1801. François returned to the United States the same year under orders from the French government to strip and sell the two nurseries and replace them with native agents in the principal seaports. In 1802, he spent the summer traveling throughout what was then thought of as the western United States including Ohio. He later gave an account of his trip in his *Voyage a l'Ouest des Monts Alléghanys dans les États de l'Ohio, du Kentucky et du Tennessée, et retour a Charleston* published, after his return to France, in 1804.

François returned to the United States in 1806 after being captured enroute by the British and held for a time in Bermuda. After three years of further travel and study along the East Coast, he returned to France, where he spent the remainder of his life. It was there that from 1810 to 1813 he oversaw the publication of his *Histoire des Arbres Forestiers de l'Amérique Septentrionale*, the first large detailed study of American trees. The work acquired more widespread usage in America with the appearance of A. L. Hillhouse's English translation of the work as *The North American Sylva* (1819). The Cleveland collections also have the rare *Histoire des Pins et des Sapins de l'Amérique Septentrionale,* published in 1810, which appears to be a separate issue of the first two livraisons of the

Histoire des Arbres Forestiers but with the order of names on the plates altered from the larger work.

The continuing influence of the Linnaean system in the United States is reflected in Henry Muhlenberg's (also known as Gotthilf Heinrich Ernst Muehlenberg) pioneer attempt to formulate an American flora based on the Linnaean system in his ***Catalogus Plantarum Americae Septentrionalis*** published at Lancaster, Pa. in 1813. The Cleveland collections also have Muhlenberg's ***Descriptio Uberior Graminum et Plantarum Calamariarum Americae Septentrionalis Indigenarum et Cicurum***, his work on American grasses published in 1817.

Botanical education in the United States is represented by a number of works in the collections. Benjamin Waterhouse, the American physician who was professor of the theory and practice of medicine at Harvard and later medical superintendent of all the military posts in New England is represented by ***The Botanist***, a compilation of the botanical portion of his lectures on natural history, which was published together with his ***The Principle of Vitality*** in 1811. Three years later, Jacob Bigelow, who also taught at Harvard, produced a regional flora intended for the use of his classes in botany and the materia medica under the title ***Florula Bostoniensis*** in 1814. The work in its original edition was limited to plants growing within a ten mile radius of Boston. Cleveland has a presentation copy from Bigelow of the original edition as well as a copy of the second edition published in 1824, in which Bigelow, with the assistance of Dr. Francis Boott, extended the work to cover all of New England.

Also associated with the American academic botanists is the German, Frederick Pursh (or Friedrich Traugott Pursch). Pursh studied horticulture under the court gardener of his native Saxony, where he worked on the staff of the Royal Botanic Garden at Dresden before coming to the United States. In America, he worked as a gardener at estates in Maryland and Pennsylvania before being employed on botanizing expeditions for Benjamin Smith Barton. He worked briefly as gardener at the Elgin Botanic Garden, which Dr. David Hosack had set up in New York City for his courses in materia medica at Columbia College, but left the post to recuperate from an illness in the Lesser Antilles. Upon his return to New York, he found Hosack out of funds, and with no job available, he went to England. There he enjoyed the patronage of A. L. Lambert, and this support allowed him to publish his ***Flora Americae Septentrionalis*** in 1814. It was the first North American flora to include plants from the Pacific coast, access to which Pursh obtained through his acquaintance with Bernard M'Mahon, the Philadelphia nurseryman entrusted with the specimens brought back from the Lewis and Clark expedition. Unfortunately, two years later Pursh left the relative comfort of his English position to botanize in Canada and compose a Canadian flora. There the materials for the flora were destroyed in a fire and Pursh himself died destitute in Montreal.

Pursh was only one of a number of foreign botanists who passed through or settled in the early United States. Others represented in the collections include Baron Ambroise Marie François Joseph Palisot de Beauvois and Constantine Samuel Rafinesque. Although Palisot de Beauvois does not appear to have had any major influence on American botany, his trips to this country were under interesting circumstances. Palisot was born to a noble family, served as a musketeer, studied law, and served as *Receveur Général des Domaines et Bois* in Northern France until the post was suppressed in 1777. After studying botany with Jussieu, Palisot spent four years in Benin with a group sent to establish a French trading post. This was followed by two stints in what is present day Haiti, split by a visit to the United States, where he attempted to raise funds to suppress

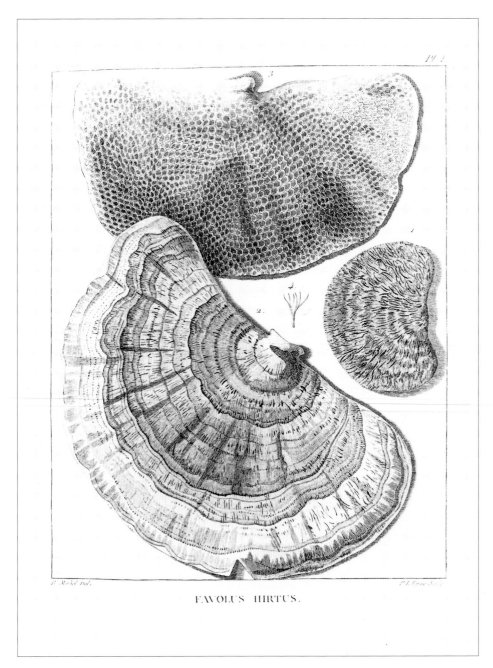

FAVOLUS HIRTUS, engraving by P. L'Epine after B. Mirbel. Ambroise Marie
François Joseph Palisot de Beauvois, *Flora d'Oware et de Benin*, 1803. (HA).

black uprisings. His second stay in Haiti ended
with his expulsion. He returned to the United
States, where he earned a living as a street mu-
sician in Philadelphia until Caspar Wistar, the
Quaker physician, employed him to arrange the
natural history cabinet of Charles Willson Peale,
the painter. He finally returned to France only
to find all his property confiscated as a result
of the revolution. Although the Cleveland collections do not have anything bearing on his
stint in the United States, they do have one of
five known copies of the one fascicle issued of
the quarto version of his *Flore d'Oware et de
Benin*. This was published in 1803, but was
abandoned in favor of the folio version. There
is also a series of separately issued off-prints
of botanical journal articles issued between
1808 and 1816 and dealing mainly with the

sexual organs of mosses, tree physiology, and sap flow and the xylem.

Constantine Rafinesque, the son of a French merchant and a Greek mother of German heritage, was born in Constantinople. Largely self-taught, he displayed a voracious, if undisciplined, desire for knowledge in a number of fields, but is best remembered for his efforts in botany and natural history. His careers included time spent as a merchant's apprentice, in a Philadelphia counting house, as secretary to the United States consul to Italy, in various publishing enterprises, in producing medicinal squills, as a tutor, in banking and inventing, and eight years as professor of botany, natural history, and modern languages at the University of Transylvania in Kentucky.

The Cleveland collections possess a copy of his *Caratteri di Alcuni Nuovi Generi e Nuove Specie di Animali e Piante della Sicilia* published in 1809 and 1810 while he was in Sicily, his *Principes Fondamenteaux de Somiologie* published in 1814, in which he set about to make basic reforms in the nomenclature of both plants and animals, and his *Circular Address on Botany and Zoology* (1816) circulated to all the museums and collectors of the United States. In the latter, Rafinesque offered to act as agent for collectors and authors, to identify specimens, to trade specimens, and to trade his writings for books in an attempt to rebuild collections which he lost in a shipwreck. His translation and revision of Claude C. Robin's *Florula Ludoviciana* published in 1817, is also here. In this work, Rafinesque "rectifies the errors" of Robin in this flora of Louisiana, vastly reducing the size of the text, but retaining the original natural classification scheme in the manner of Jussieu, and adding a list of Louisiana plants not recorded by Robin.

Another foreigner who played an important role in the history of early American botany was Thomas Nuttall, the English botanist and ornithologist. After apprenticing as a printer,

Nuttall came to the United States to gather botanical specimens for Benjamin Smith Barton. He went on to explore the botany of the Missouri River with his fellow British botanist, John Bradbury. Later he made botanical expeditions exploring the Arkansas and Red Rivers, and accompanied the Wyeth expedition to the mouth of the Columbia River, returning by way of California, Hawaii, and Cape Horn. He served from 1822 to 1832 as curator of the botanical garden at Harvard, where he also gave lectures on botany. When he returned to England, he spent the remainder of his life raising rhododendrons on an inherited estate. He is represented in Cleveland by his 1818 *The Genera of North American Plants* that was written after the Missouri expedition of 1809 to 1811 but delayed in publication by the fact that Nuttall had returned to England and could not return to the United States until the conclusion of the War of 1812. The work was important both because of the new species introduced from the expedition and because he used A. L. de Jussieu's system of genera to organize the plants.

A later product of Nuttall's work is the first edition of his *An Introduction to Systematic and Physiological Botany* (1827). The work was important because it was deliberately written in a less technical manner than other American introductions to botany, using the letters on botany of Jean Jacques Rousseau and Thomas Martyn as models. (The Cleveland collections include the 1794 English edition of Rousseau's *Letters on the Elements of Botany Addressed to a Lady* and the large and small format editions of the French form published as *La Botanique* in 1805, as well as the 1794 edition of Thomas Martyn's *Twenty-Four Additional Letters*). The second part of the work is an abridgement of Anthony Thomson's *Lectures on the Elements of Botany,* the original of which was published in London in 1822.

The Harvard botanical garden, where Nuttall had served as curator, was founded in 1807 by William Dandridge Peck. Peck was an unusual figure who retired from an accounting house at an early age to join his father in his retirement on a secluded farm in Maine, where he spent 20 years studying the local wildlife. Word spread of his knowledge and led to a circle of his friends raising the money to establish a professorship in natural history for him at Harvard, a position he assumed after a trip to Europe to gather books, information, and specimens. He is represented in the collections by an 1818 issue of his *A Catalogue of American and Foreign Plants Cultivated in the Botanic Garden*, a guide to the plants in the Harvard botanical garden.

A Synopsis of the Genera of American Plants is a pocket sized reference work first published in 1814 that could easily be taken into the field. It is generally believed to have been written by Obadiah Rich, the American botanist, bibliographer, diplomat, and antiquarian. The copy here is of particular interest since it belonged to Jared Potter Kirtland, the noted physician, naturalist, and founder of Case Western Reserve University's School of Medicine. It contains a contemporary list of genera omitted by Rich in Kirtland's handwriting.

American editions of English publications, often with modifications or added material by American botanists, also played a part in the corpus of educational botanical works. This tendency is represented in the collections by two works originally written by Sir James Edward Smith. His *An Introduction to Physiological and Systematical Botany* in the first American edition of 1814 was based on the second English edition which was edited and annotated by Jacob Bigelow. Smith's *A Grammar of Botany, Illustrative of Artificial, as well as Natural Classification, with an Explanation of Jussieu's System* (1822) was originally written to supply the definitions for the terms used in Smith's *An*

Introduction to Physiological and Systematical Botany. As will be noted by the subject matter, by this time the importance of the natural system was even being acknowledged by Smith, the President of the Linnean Society. This fact was further brought home by the accompaniment of the work in this American edition with Henry Muhlenberg's *Reduction of All the Genera Contained in the Catalogue of North American Plants, to the Natural Families of the French Professor*.

The great popularizer of botany in the nineteenth century United States was Amos Eaton. Eaton, who was to become best known for his work in botany, geology, and education, began his career as a lawyer and land agent in the Catskill region of New York. This activity was cut short by his conviction on forgery charges which resulted in his imprisonment from 1811 to 1815 and subsequent banishment from the state of New York until his unconditional pardon in 1817. In prison, Eaton returned to the study of botany and geology which he had previously begun under the tutelage of David Hosack and Samuel Mitchell. Following his release, he studied at Yale under Professors Elie Ives and Benjamin Silliman, Sr. and earned teaching certificates, that allowed him to become an itinerant lecturer throughout New York and New England. At various times, he served as lecturer in natural history at the Lyceum of Natural History at Troy, New York, and as professor of natural history in the Medical School at Castleton, Vermont. His educational doctrine was one of learning by doing. Students were left to collect and analyze their own specimens, and even give their own lectures with the instructor and fellow students acting primarily as critics. His method of teaching was employed at Rensselaer Institute, where Eaton served as senior professor and principal.

His most famous book is his *Manual of Botany* that first appeared anonymously in 1817 as *A Manual of Botany for the Northern States*.

The Cleveland collections also include the second edition of 1818 in which Eaton's name appears on the title page for the first time and the title is enlarged to *A Manual of Botany for the Northern and Middle States*. The fourth edition was published in 1824 as *A Manual of Botany for the Northern and Middle States of America* with an appendix by Lewis Beck, added species cited by John Torrey, and lichens noted by Dr. Halsey. The fifth edition composed by Eaton, William Edward A. Aikin, and Hezekiah Hulbert Eaton, under the title of *A Manual of Botany for North America,* expanded the area covered to all states north of the Gulf of Mexico.

Also in the collections are copies of the 1817 edition of Eaton's translation of the work by Louis-Claude Marie Richard published as *A Botanical Dictionary* with additions from the writings of Martyn, Smith, Milne, Willdenow, and Acharius, and the 1828 translation by Eaton of the work by Richard and Pierre Bulliard published as *A Botanical Grammar and Dictionary*. Both of these were intended by Eaton to supplement the various editions of his *Manual*.

Material from the *Manual* and *Botanical Dictionary* was drawn together and condensed to form the basis of Eaton's *Botanical Exercises* first published in 1820. This pioneer textbook of botanical exercises was published without plates to keep it affordable enough for purchase by most students of botany. Eaton did, however include advice on conducting a course in botany.

Eaton's pupil, Almira Hart Lincoln (afterwards Phelps), became vice-principal of the Troy Female Seminary in Troy, New York, where she composed *Familiar Lectures on Botany* first published in 1829. The work sold over 275,000 copies over 40 years and was especially popular as a text for use in girls' schools since it removed some botanical terms derived from parts of the human body and omitted the more graphic sexual language of Linnaeus.

Another botanist influenced by Eaton was John Torrey, whose father was the fiscal agent at the prison where Eaton served his sentence. Torrey, who became the chief American proponent of the natural system expounded by A. L. de Jussieu and A. P. de Candolle, was at various times a physician, botanist, chemist, geologist, and assayer. His appointments included terms as professor of chemistry, mineralogy, and geology at West Point, an appointment as professor of chemistry at the College of Physicians and Surgeons (New York), and one as professor of chemistry and natural history at Princeton. He is represented in Cleveland by the first edition of *A Compendium of the Flora of the Northern and Middle States* (1826) which described the plants listed in his *Flora of the Northern and Middle States of the United States* published three years earlier.

The collections contain one work on palaeobotany printed before 1829. This is the second edition of Johann Jacob Scheuchzer's *Herbarium Diluvianum* (1723). Scheuchzer was a Swiss physician whose career included periods as the assistant municipal physician at Zurich, medical superior of the Zurich orphanage, professor of mathematics, head of the Bibliothèque des Bourgeois, and director of the Zurich museum of natural history. Although Scheuchzer was preceded by the Welshman, Edward Llwyd, who published several pictures of plant fossils from the Ashmolean collection in 1699, the first edition of the *Herbarium Diluvianum* (1709) is generally regarded as the first really comprehensive and well-illustrated book on fossil plants. The second edition (the one present in Cleveland) is valued for containing four more plates of illustrations than the first. As the title suggests, Scheuchzer was another in the long line of pious botanists marveling at God's creations, which in this case were taken to be preserved biological records from the Biblical flood. Still, this was a more radical view than that taken by other geologists of the period who regarded fossils as *formed rocks* that simply resembled other natural forms. The work was of sufficient importance to establish Scheuchzer as the father of Swiss, and in the views of some, of European palaeobotany.

A more philosophical work was that of Johann Wolfgang von Goethe in his neo-platonistic ***Versuch die Metamorphose der Pflanzen zu erklären*** (1790). The author, who is best remembered for his literary and philosophical works, also worked extensively in zoology, botany, and geology. In the ***Versuch die Metamorphose der Pflanzen,*** Goethe put forth two ideas that would have a significant effect on the development of evolutionary theory. The first of these concerned the concept of metamorphosis, or the natural transformation of a single organ into varying forms to fulfill varying functions. Thus the same organ originally found as a leaf will change its shape and function to become a *calyx*, a petal, the sexual organs, and the fruit of the plant. The second concept was that of an *Urpflanz,* an archetypical plant from which all other plants are derived through modification of its parts. Although much longer on philosophical reflection than on scientific experiment or examination, the work provoked a great deal of thought among the botanists of Goethe's generation and of the succeeding generation, and it is often cited as the work which founded the science of morphology.

Another German who was to have a major influence throughout all the sciences was Baron Friedrich Heinrich Alexander von Humboldt, who, accompanied by the French botanist and physician, Aimée Jacques Alexandre Goujand Bonpland, embarked on an expedition to explore Venezuela, Cuba, Colombia, Peru, Ecuador, and Mexico that lasted from 1799 through 1804. In the course of their exploration, Humboldt and Bonpland made maps, collected specimens, and amassed data in the fields of magnetism, meteorology, climatology, geology, mineralogy, oceanography, zoology, botany, and ethnography. The information was so extensive that it took 32 years to publish the data assembled by the expedition as the 36 volume ***Voyage aux Régions Équinoxiales du Nouveau Continent.*** It earned the title of the *scientific discovery of America.* The botanical discoveries of the trip are represented in Cleveland by three of the 18 volumes of the botanical section, the two volume ***Plantes Équinoxiales,*** bearing publication dates of 1808 through 1809 (but actually published from 1805 through 1817), and the one volume ***Monographie des Melastomacées,*** published from 1806 through 1816.

Among Humboldt's many accomplishments were his introduction of guano into Europe and his establishment of the field of plant geography. The latter achievement is represented in the collections by his ***De Distributione Geographica Plantarum Secundum Coeli Temperiem et Altitudinem Montium, Prolegomena*** published in 1817. The collections also include a less erudite discussion on the same subject in the form of John Barton's ***A Lecture on the Geography of Plants*** published in 1827, but originally delivered as a lecture to the Mechanic's Institute of Chichester.

CHAPTER III

Botanical Illustration

THE EARLIEST BOTANICAL ILLUSTRATIONS in the Cleveland collections are those found in the **Herbarium** of Apuleius printed in 1483 or earlier. These anonymous pictures, although crude in appearance, are believed by some to reflect a late Roman school of botanical illustration. In many instances, they feature, along with the highly stylized plant, an image of an animal whose bite the plant was believed to cure. The grainy texture of the pictures has suggested that they were made from metal rather than wood blocks.

The more normal form of early illustration is the woodcut as found in the editions of the **Herbarius Latinus** and **Hortus Sanitatis**. The pictures are crude, symmetrical, and generally lacking in both realism and any but the most blatant botanical details.

A much more realistic and detailed set of wood cuts is the work of the anonymous cutter employed to illustrate Brunfels' **Herbarum Vivae Eicones** or "living pictures of plants." The pictures, which are much more important than the accompanying text, were made from the

original designs of Hans Weiditz and accurately portray the specimens available to him down to such details as torn leaves. The Cleveland

CALAMUS SILVESTRIS, woodcut. **Herbarius Latinus**, 1491. (GC).

Kreüterbüch.　　LXVII

Aron.　　Aron traub.
F iiij

ARON, woodcut by Hans Weiditz.
Otto Brunfels, *Contrafayt Kreüterbuch,* 1532.
(CMLA).

collections feature Weiditz's realistic approach to botanical subjects in Brunfels' *Herbarum Vivae Eicones,* in the German version published as the *Contrafayt Kreüterbuch* in 1532, and in *In Dioscoridis Historiam Herbarum Certissima Adaptio.* The latter is a collection of the woodcuts published in 1543 from the Brunfels herbals and limited to plants mentioned by Dioscorides. A more diversified set of woodcut panels attributed to Weiditz is found in a collection of dietetic and pharmacological works beginning with Ibn Butlan's *Tacuini Sanitatis* published in 1531.

A more idealized realism is found in the illustrations of the works of Leonhart Fuchs. The pictures were drawn from nature by Albrecht Meyer, transferred to woodblocks by Heinrich Füllmaurer, and cut onto the wood by Veit Rudolf Speckle, all of whom, along with Fuchs,

have been immortalized through a series of woodcut portraits. The large elegant pictures often represent a combination of specimens in order to show both the fruit and flower at the same time or to display the flowers of several different species on a single plant for the sake of economy. The pictures were deliberately done in outline without shading so that they could be readily hand-colored. The Cleveland collections are especially rich in their holdings of Fuchs illustrations and include copies of the *De Historia Stirpium* of 1542 (including one which has been identified as a copy issued colored by the original artists), its German version, the *New Kreüterbuch* of 1543, a unique collection of 510 proofs before letters of the illustrations for the *New Kreüterbuch,* 60 woodcuts intended for the continuation of the *New Kreüterbuch* (which was never published), and 19 colored reprints from the blocks of the *De Historia Stirpium.* The latter were apparently part of those published at Zurich in 1774 by Salomon Schinz as part of his *Anleitung zu der Pflanzenkenntniss und derselben nützlichsten*

TITLE PAGE. *In Dioscoridis Historiam,* 1543. (HA).

Anwendung. By way of contrast, the collections also contain the French translation entitled *Histoire des Plantes Reduicte en Tres Bon Ordre* published by Pesnot at Lyons in 1575 and featuring reduced and reversed copies of the original illustrations.

As we have noted earlier, Hieronymus Bock, the third of the German fathers of botany, provided such detailed descriptions of the plants in his herbal that no illustrations were deemed necessary when the **New Kreütter Buch** first appeared in 1539. Beginning with the second German edition, the **Kreuter Buch** of 1546, however, illustrations were added. The artist was a young self-taught illustrator named David Kandel. Most of the illustrations either copy those found in Fuchs's **De Historia Stirpium** or, when original, are done in the same style. In general, due to the smaller format of the illustrations they suffer in comparison with those used by Fuchs.

BELLEN/ PAPPELBAUM, woodcut by David Kandel. Hieronymus Bock, **Kreuter Buch,** 1546. (CMLA).

HAND-COLORED UNPUBLISHED WOODCUT presumed to be by Veit Rudolf Speckle and Heinrich Füllmaurer after Albrecht Meyer for an intended continuation of Leonhart Fuchs's **New Kreuterbuch.** (HA).

Beginning with the illustration for chapter 27 of Bock's second book, non-botanical elements begin to appear with the presence of a pair of ducks at the base of the plants being portrayed. A crane and frogs complement the plant in chapter 36 and a pair of small birds hover about and dine on the seeds of the thistle portrayed in chapter 106. In Bock's third book, the menagerie continues with more birds, squirrels, charming rabbits, a fox, a beetle, fish, a crayfish, a monkey, and even a unicorn gracing various woodcuts of plants. A hedgehog is contrasted with the prickly covering of the chesnut, the serpent coils around the apple tree next to a skull and bone, and the association of boxwood with Easter Sunday in Northern Europe is commemorated by the portrayal of a demon fleeing from the crowing cock beneath the box tree.

Humans are also incorporated into Kandel's universe in rather graphic detail. Their depictions range from the elegant lady standing beneath the tree in chapter 32 and the lively, but relatively refined, pastoral scenes of chapters 72 and 74, to the dour swineherd overseeing his charges as they devour acorns, the inelegant lady perched in a tree throwing cherries to her companion who immodestly catches them in her lifted skirt, and the graphic depiction of the dual purgative effects of the fig.

The story of Pyramus and Thisbe is reflected both in Bock's text and Kandel's illustration for the mulberry. The lovers planned tryst was interrupted by the appearance of a lioness who frightened Thisbe away. Pyramus then arrived on the scene and found Thisbe's veil, which she had dropped, and concluded that she had been killed by the animal. He then killed himself, and Thisbe, in turn, killed herself upon finding her lover's body. Their blood stained the white flowers of the mulberry purple and accounts for their present color. Somewhat more perplexing in its meaning is the animal skin garbed hunter about to bash a befanged beaver in the illustration of the white poplar.

The next series of celebrated woodcuts in the collections were those made to illustrate the various editions of the **Commentarii** on Dioscorides of Mattioli. There are two sets of cuts involved. The small set first appeared in a Latin edition of 1554 published by Valgrisi in Venice. Although this is not in the Cleveland collections, the small set appears here in a 1555 Italian edition. The more celebrated large set first appears in the German edition published at Prague as the **New Kreüterbuch** by Melantrich and Valgrisi in 1563. The small set has been ascribed by Sandra Raphael[1] to Giorgio Liberale, while the large set has been ascribed to Liberale and George Meyerpeck in the **Epistola Nuncupatoria** of the 1565 Latin **Commentarii**. The cuts themselves are generally botanically accurate but with a strong decorative element that manifests itself in the extension of plant foliage to fill the whole surface of some blocks and sometimes in an overabundance of shading in the form of crosshatching.

At least some of the Mattioli woodblocks have survived to the present day with some 110 having been offered for sale as recently as 1989. Although much of the history of the blocks has been lost, we do know that many of them were acquired by Henri Duhamel du Monceau, the French authority on trees, who used some of them, along with engraved headpieces of the trees' flowers and seeds, to illustrate his **Traité des Arbres et Arbustes** published in 1755.

The woodcuts used in the 1586 edition of Mattioli's **De Plantis Epitome,** edited by Joachim Camerarius, are important for their early detailing of flower and fruit parts. The illustrations probably puzzled the contemporary readers since no mention of these details appears in the text. This is because the sketches for the woodcuts were originally prepared for Conrad Gesner's unfinished history of botany. After Gesner's death, they were left in the care of his friend, Kaspar Wolf, who had the woodcuts made and was supposed to prepare the work for publication. However, Wolf sold the sketches, woodcuts, and Gesner's other botanical effects to Joachim Camerarius the Younger. He used them, along with others which he had made himself, to illustrate the Mattioli and other works which he wrote or edited. Others of the unused drawings and blocks were obtained by Christoph Jakob Trew. He published the useable woodcuts, engraved copies of the unuseable blocks done by Michael Seligmann, and the surviving botanical texts of Gesner as Gesner's **Opera Botanica** (1751 through 1771).

[1]Blunt, Wilfred and Sandra Raphael. *The Illustrated Herbal*. New York: Thames and Hudson, Inc. and the Metropolitan Museum of Art, 1979.

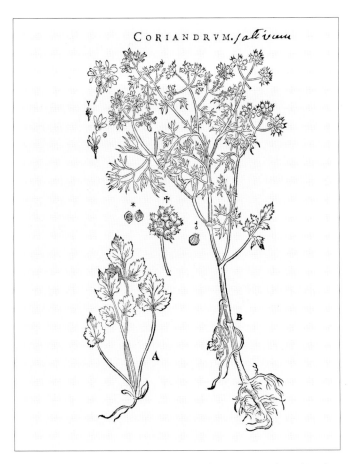

CORIANDRUM, woodcut. Pier Andrea Mattioli, edited
by J. Camerarius, *De Plantes Epitome,* 1586.
(CMLA).

The illustrations of the *Herbario
Novo* of Castore Durante, by contrast,
are mainly modeled in their botanical
details on the woodcuts used by Fuchs
and Mattioli. The figures, which were
originally drawn by Isabella Parasole
with the blocks cut by Leonardo
Norsino, are not botanically distinguished but have a certain charm owing to their simplicity and the picturesque landscapes, animals, and people
which accompany some of the plants.

The most widely used set of botanical woodcuts of the late sixteenth
and early seventeenth centuries is the
group of small cuts assembled by the
Plantin printing house for use in illustrating the botanical works of Dodoens,
Clusius (L'Ecluse), and L'Obel. The
chief artist employed by Plantin was
Pieter van der Borcht of Malines who
is first found doing the illustrations for
Plantin's edition of Dodoens's *Frumentorum, Leguminum, et Herbarum Historia*
published in 1566. He is also responsible for the designs of the illustrations
in Dodoens's *Florum et Nonnullarum
Herbarum Historia* (1568),
Clusius's *Rariorum aliquot
Stirpium per Pannonium et
Austriam Observatarum
Historia* (1583 [-1584]),
and 52 of the illustrations
for Clusius's *Rariorum aliquot Stirpium per Hispanias
Observatarum Historia*
(1576). The rest of the
illustrations in the latter

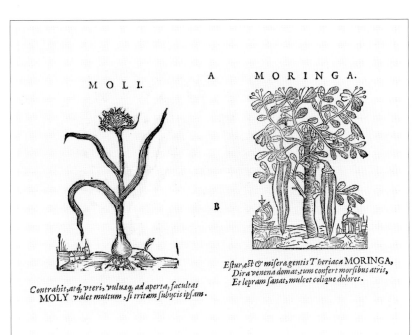

Contrahit, atq̃ vteri, vulu&q̃; ad aperta, facultas
MOLY valet multum, ſi tritam ſubycis ipſam.

Eſtur, eſt & miſeræ gentis Theriaca MORINGA,
Dira venena domat, tum confert morſibus atris,
Et lepram ſanat, mulcet colique dolores.

MOLY and **MORINGA,**
woodcuts by Leonardo
Norsino after Isabella
Parasole. Castore
Durante, *Herbario
Nova,* 1602. (HA).

were after the original drawings of Clusius. The artists who cut the designs onto the wooden blocks included Cornelius Muller, Gerard van Kampen, Arnaud Nicolai, and Antony van Leest. Besides these and other blocks commissioned by the printer, the Plantin stock also contained a number of blocks obtained from other printers. These included the blocks used in the works of Dodoens, previously published by Jean Loë and acquired from his widow, and 250 of the blocks from Pena and Lobel's *Stirpium Adversaria Nova* of 1570-1571, purchased from Thomas Purfoot.

The Plantin stock, together with the earlier cuts used in Fuchs, Bock, and Mattioli, served as models for yet another set of small woodcuts which was first used in the *Neuw Kreuterbuch* of Tabernaemontanus published from 1587 through 1591. The chief interest in this stock lies in the fact that it was acquired by Edmond Norton for use in his publication of the 1597[-1598] first edition of John Gerard's *Herball or Generall Historie of Plants.*

*T*HUS FAR IN OUR discussion of botanical illustration we have been chiefly concerned with herbals. A second class of heavily illustrated botanical works is that of the florilegium. The term florilegium literally means a grouping of flowers. For purposes of our discussion it is applied to heavily illustrated botanical works with little or no accompanying text, although botanically the term is also sometimes used to denote lists of plants in place of the more common term, flora. Florilegia can take many forms including plant catalogues, model books for illustrators in various media, field guides for plant identification, commemorations of exceptional plants and exceptional gardens, coloring books, and books simply dedicated to handsome botanical illustration.

Several of the sets of woodcuts already mentioned were used in florilegia. The illustrations from the rather thick two-volume herbal of Tabernaemontanus were gathered together and published without text as *Eicones Plantarum* in an oblong quarto in 1590. The Plantin stock used to illustrate the works of Pena and L'Obel was also separately published without text as *Icones Stirpium seu Plantarum tam Exoticarum, quam Indigenarum* in 1591. In both instances, the works were probably aimed on the one hand at the artistic market which would not require the medical and botanical details of the text, and on the other hand at the practicing student of botany, pharmacology, or medicine, who would need something less bulky and more portable than the full-fledged work for use in identifying and gathering specimens in the field.

At the end of the sixteenth century the use of the woodcut for botanical illustration was largely supplanted by engravings, etchings, and the more common combination of the two processes. One of the two printed works usually cited as the first book to contain floral engravings is the *Florilegium* prepared by the Belgian engraver Adrian Collaert and published circa 1590. Unlike the previously mentioned florilegia, this work consisted of original groupings of flowers published for the first time and was intended as a pattern book for the portrayal of plants by artists in various media.

According to many of the writers on botanical illustration the first important florilegium was Pierre Vallet's *Le Jardin du Roy Tres Chrestien Henry IV* published in 1608. Vallet was a French artist and engraver who styled himself as "brodeur ordinaire" (embroiderer in ordinary) to Henry IV of France. The work, which was intended as a pattern-book for Marie de Médicis and the ladies of her court to use in their embroidery, features large elegant flowers realistically portrayed, although perhaps a bit heavily shaded for some tastes.

FOUR LEAVES OF ENGRAVINGS by Adrian Collaert. Adrian Collaert, *Florilegium,* circa 1590. (HA).

ENGRAVING by Johann Theodor de Bry. Johann Theodor de Bry, *Anthologia Magna,* 1626. (CMLA).

ETCHINGS OF FRITILLARIES by Pierre Vallet. Pierre Vallet, *Le Jardin du Roy Tres Chrestien Henri IV,* 1608. (CMLA).

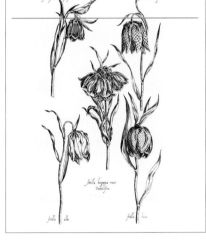

As Wilfred Blunt[2] pointed out, some of Vallet's plates were copied in reverse in a number of florilegia produced by Johann Theodor de Bry and Matthaeus Merian. De Bry, who was the son of the better known artist Theodor de Bry, published the second edition or issue of his *Florilegium Novum* from 1612 through 1614. After his death, the work was expanded and issued as the *Anthologia Magna* in 1626, and was further expanded by his son-in-law, Matthaeus Merian, who added plates adapted from the *De Florum Cultura Libri IV* of Giovanni Baptista Ferrari in the edition published as *Florilegium Renovatum* in 1641. Although relying on Vallet's work for some of their inspiration, the plates primarily engraved by de Bry and Merian have a stiff formal feel when compared to the primarily etched plates of Vallet.

The Cleveland collections also feature late editions of two works illustrated by Maria Sibylla Merian, the daughter of Matthaeus Merian and granddaughter of Johann Theodor de Bry. It is not surprising that Maria, whose stepfather was Jacob Marrell, the Dutch floral painter, should show an artistic bent; her chosen subject matter, however, was unexpected, since from an early age she devoted herself to portraying all varieties of insects in their various stages. She is considered one of the finest botanical artists of the late seventeenth to early eighteenth centuries because of her portrayal of the flora accompanying her insects.

[2]Wilfred Blunt is an art historian and leading expert in the field of botanical illustration. All references, unless noted otherwise, are to: Blunt, Wilfred, with the assistance of William T. Stern. *The New Naturalist: The Art of Botanical Illustration.* 3rd ed. London: Collins, 1955.

ENGRAVED PLATE by Maria Sibylla Merian. Maria Sibylla Merian, French translation by J. Marret, *Histoire des Insectes de l'Europe,* 1730. (HA).

ENGRAVED TITLE PAGE. Emanuel Sweert, *Florilegium,* 1612. (CMLA).

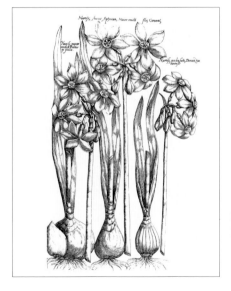

ENGRAVINGS OF NARCISSES. Emanuel Sweert, *Florilegium,* 1612. (CMLA).

Cleveland has a 1730 edition of Merian's *Histoire des Insectes de l'Europe* and a circa 1745 edition of her *Receuil de Plantes des Indes*. Although the *Receuil* is marred by rather crude hand-coloring, the fine detail of her work is very evident in the uncolored *Histoire*.

The year 1612, which saw the initial publication of de Bry's work, also saw the publication of the *Florilegium* of Emanuel Sweert, a Dutch florist who at one time served as prefect of gardens for Emperor Rudolph II. The engravings, which have sometimes been attributed to Sweert, are much cruder and more simplistic than the other florilegia that we have discussed. The plates are nevertheless still highly prized for their decorative effect, especially in hand-colored copies. Their relative simplicity is not altogether surprising since this florilegium was not intended as the masterwork of an engraver or a copybook for artists, but rather as an illustrated catalogue showing the variety of plants which could be purchased as bulbs, seeds, or plants from Sweert's shop at the Frankfurt Fair or his shop in Amsterdam. The Cleveland collections boast five different editions or issues of the work beginning with a hand-dated edition of 1612, which may be the first edition, and ending with the edition of 1647.

Perhaps the most celebrated of the sales catalogue class of florilegia is the *Twelve Months of Flowers* published for Robert Furber in 1730. This widely reproduced work features twelve hand-colored engravings of bouquets of flowers by Henry Fletcher after original paintings by the Flemish artist Peter Casteels. Each bouquet represented the plants available from Furber, a florist of Kensington, during each month of the year. It was followed in 1732 by another illustrated catalogue featuring an arrangement of fruit for each month of the year which again represented plants available from Furber with the majority of plates again engraved by Henry Fletcher after originals by Peter Casteels.

The popularity of the plates from the *Twelve Months of Flowers* is attested to by the fact that smaller copies were engraved by James Smith and became the main feature of *The Flower-Garden Display'd* published originally in 1732. It is represented in the Cleveland collections by the second edition or issue of 1734. In this work the plates were accompanied by a descriptive text with directions on the cultivation of the plants illustrated. The text is believed to be the work of Richard Bradley. The book was issued with hand-colored plates, which, it is at pains to point out, differ from the colors used in the *Twelve Months of Flowers* since those in this later work are "taken from Nature."

A related form of florilegium is that which uses illustrations to celebrate the plants raised in specific gardens. One of the earliest of these, and certainly the largest, is the *Hortus Eystettensis* of Basilius Besler published in 1613. The work, which has been described as the "massiest" of herbals and as requiring two wheelbarrows to transport it, was compiled by Besler, a Nuremberg apothecary in charge of the lavish flower garden of Johann Konrad von Gemmingen, Prince Bishop of Eichstätt. Although Besler asserted that he spent 16 years in the preparation of the drawings for the plates, Claus Nissen[3] indicates that both the originals and the engravings are more likely the work of the engravers Johann Leypolt, Wolfgang Kilian, Servatius Raven, Levin van Hulsen, Dominic and Robert Custos (or Coster), Heinrich Ulrich, Friedrich van Hulsen, and Peter Isselburgh. The large highly ornamental plates have made the book a prime target for breakers (dealers who break-up books for their plates), with the result that framed individual plates are met with much more frequently than the complete book.

A smaller work, which is regarded by some as the finest florilegium of the seventeenth century, is the *Hortus Floridus* of Crispijn van de Passe the Younger. Crispijn was a member of a

[3]Claus Nissen is a leading bibliographic expert on botanical illustration. References are to: Nissen, Claus, Die Botanische Buchillustration ihre Geschichte und Bibliographie. Stüttgart:[H/ Laupp, Jr., Tubingen, for] Hiersemann Verlagses Co., 1950-1951.

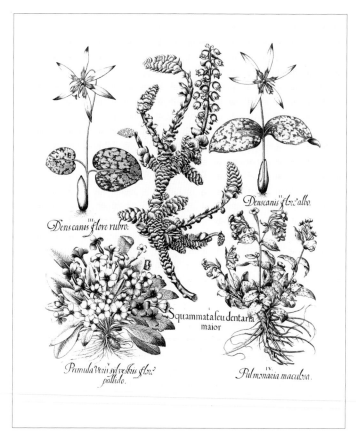

ENGRAVING. Basilius Besler, ***Hortus Eystettensis,*** 1613. (CMLA).

family of Dutch engravers. In 1617, Crispijn moved from Utrecht to Paris to serve as representative for his father's engraving house and was subsequently appointed professor of drawing at the Maneige Royal, a school for the education of royal pages and other young nobility. The work antedates the move, however, and represents an early part of Crispijn's career.

The ***Hortus Floridus*** is a bibliographically complex work. Between its initial appearance in 1614 and the final Latin issue of 1616 to 1617, there were two Latin editions, an English edition, and a Dutch edition, with several states[4] mixed in. The plates, which are primarily the work of Crispijn (although some are engraved by his brothers Simon and Willem), are organized according to the seasons of the year and display an ornamental realism reminiscent of the work of Dürer or the Dutch masters. Some of the plates were altered from one edition to another with the addition of background and insects in later states (features which were included in other plates from the beginning). The

HYPATICA TRIFOLIA CAERULEA POLYANTHUS and **HYPATICA TRIFOLIA FLORE NIVEA,** early state of the engraving by Crispijn van de Passe the Younger. Crispijn van de Passe the Younger, ***Hortus Floridus,*** 1614. (GC).

[4]Several terms, such as "states", "variant issue" and "cancel", appear in this chapter. They are technical bibliographic terms that are difficult to clearly define in a limited space. However, in a general sense, they refer to variations in issues or editions of a work.

HEPATICA TRIFOLIA CAERULAEA POLYANTHUS and **HEPATICA TRIFOLIA FLORE NIVEA** in a late state
of a hand-colored engraving by Crispijn van de Passe the Younger. Crispijn van de Passe the Younger,
Hortus Floridus, 1616-1617. (CMLA).

Cleveland collections allow one to compare the 1614 Latin version with the earliest states of the plates (at the Cleveland Botanical Garden) with the magnificently hand-colored late state plates of the 1616 to 1617 Latin version (at the Cleveland Medical Library Association's Allen Memorial Medical Library).

The next important florilegium is the ***Theatrum Florae***, first published anonymously in 1622, which is present in the Cleveland collections in the editions of 1627 and 1633. The artist responsible for the work was Daniel Rabel, a French artist best remembered for his designs for the ballet, who served as engineer in ordinary to Louis XIII for the provinces of Brie and Champagne. The work appears to be intended as a copy-book for artists in the tradition of Vallet. The plates are also reminiscent of Vallet, although they have a stiffer feeling to

them and lack the fluidity of the former's etching.

Nicolas Robert is generally regarded as one of the finest flower painters of the seventeenth century. Early in his career he was hired by Duke Gaston d'Orleans to record the collection of plants and animals that Gaston had assembled at Blois as a series of paintings on vellum. It is there that Robert is believed to have been influenced by Robert Morison to consider the scientific aspects of his botanic illustration. After Gaston's death, Robert was appointed painter in ordinary for miniatures to Louis XIV. In this capacity, he continued the series of paintings on vellum, only the subjects became the plants in the Jardin des Plantes and the animals in the menagerie at Versailles. These paintings on vellum, together with a few done earlier by Rabel, formed the initial basis for the

MARACO INDICA SEU FLOS PASSIONIS,
engraving by Daniel Rabel. Daniel Rabel,
Theatrum Florae, 1627. (CMLA).

collection known as the Vélins du Muséum.
Robert is represented in the Cleveland collections by two florilegia which were, curiously,
both published in Rome. The earliest of these
is the ***Fiori Diversi*** of 1640, which is Robert's
first published work and was done before he
had acquired his reputation and his interest in
the scientific side of botanical illustration. The
second volume, ***Variae ac Multiformes Florum Species Expressae ad Vivum***, was published in 1665,
after his appointment as painter to Louis XIV.
It seems to make a point of displaying flowers
which are sufficiently opened to allow views of
their pistils and stamens, often accompanied
by insects.

Two other florilegia also published at Rome
during the same period are the ***Giardini di Fiori***
(circa 1640) and the ***Nova Racolta di Fiori Cavati
da Naturale Dati in Luce*** (1649). Both of these
works were engraved and published by Giovanni
Jacomo Rossi, an Italian etcher and engraver

who also published a number of illustrated
works on Italian gardens and fountains (some
of which are also in the Cleveland collections).
The plates are primarily etchings, reminiscent
of Robert, which may be significant since the
Italian publisher of Robert's plates was another
Rossi of Rome.

As we have observed, Nicolas Robert was
the first of a line of French botanical painters
to have an appointment to illustrate the specimens grown at the Jardin des Plantes. His im-
mediate successor in this post was Jean Joubert,
who did not see much of his artistic work published. The Cleveland collections do have a
single plate after Joubert that was published in
the ***Histoire Universelle du Règne Végétal*** of [1774-]
1775-1780. This massive work is one of a number of illustrated botanical books cranked out
by Pierre Joseph Buc'hoz, the French physician
and naturalist who served at various times as
doctor to the King of Poland, doctor to the
brother of the King of France, and doctor to

NARCISO GIALLO IN ORO and **SPORONIDI
CAVALIERO DOPPIJ,** engraving by Nicolas
Robert. Nicolas Robert, ***Fiori Diversi,***
1640. (CMLA).

the Duke of Artois. In general, the botanical works of Buc'hoz are not highly regarded owing to his tendencies to lift material from other sources, the general inaccuracy of his descriptions, and his tendency to recycle both texts and illustrations from one publication to another. The *Histoire Universelle* also features six plates after Claude Aubriet, Joubert's successor at the Jardin des Plantes.

The collections also have several florilegiums published for Buc'hoz. *Le Jardin d'Eden* with a publication date of 1783, but with plates dated from 1781 through 1784, displays decorative illustrations of the ornamental plants grown in the Garden of Eden of the Trianon at Versailles. It also includes two groups with separate title pages entitled *Collection Coloriée des Plus Belles Variétés de Tulipes* and *Collection Coloriée des Plus Belles Variétés de Jacinthes*. These were probably separately published in 1781, the date on their title pages.

More interesting is a two volume set published by Buc'hoz from 1776 through 1779 entitled *Collection Precieuse et Enluminée des Fleurs*. The work is intended as an illustration model for naturalists, artists, and porcelain painters and features one volume of oriental plants and one volume of plants then current in European gardens (including African and American introductions). Both groups of plants are given an oriental treatment and are particularly striking in the hand-colored copy at the Holden Arboretum.

By contrast, true oriental art is represented by a collection of 100 original paintings of birds and plants done circa 1710 by the Japanese artist, Mitsunari Tosa.

To return to the vélins, Claude Aubriet was hired at an early age to assist Joubert in their preparation. Aubriet soon attracted the attention of Joseph Pitton de Tournefort, who was at that time professor of botany at the Jardin des Plantes. As a result, the first published work to bear Aubriet illustrations was Tournefort's revolutionary *Elémens de Botanique* of 1694. The engravings featured highly detailed flower dissections, the originals of which are believed to have been prepared by Aubriet under Tournefort's close supervision. The bond between Tournefort and Aubriet was further strengthened by their scientific journey to the Levant from 1700 to 1702. Some years after their return, and upon the death of Joubert, Aubriet was appointed as Joubert's successor as painter of the vélins at the Jardin.

Aubriet is also represented in the Cleveland collections by two printed works published in Holland. The earlier of these is the 1727 *Botanicon Parisiense* written by Sebastien Vaillant, who had been one of Tournefort's pupils. Vaillant served as secretary to Guy Fagon and through his support became demonstrator of plants and was placed in charge of the garden of the Jardin des Plantes. An innovator, Vaillant is held to have been responsible for the establishment of the herbarium of the Cabinet du Roi, the construction of the first hothouse in France in 1714, and the establishment of the doctrine of sexuality in plants in France through a series of lectures and demonstrations in 1717. Vaillant spent 36 years in the preparation of this work and its prodromus, during which time Aubriet prepared its illustrations. The book on the plants of Paris was finally published in Holland through the efforts of Herman Boerhaave, who had obtained the manuscripts of both this work and its prodromus with the aid of William Sherard. It finally appeared five years after Vaillant's death with Aubriet's illustrations masterfully translated into plates by Jan Wandelaar, whom many consider to be the best natural history engraver of his time.

Boerhaave also employed Aubriet to copy the pictures made by Charles Plumier. These copies were purchased after Boerhaave's death by Jan Burmann. Burmann had engravings made from them which he published with his own descriptions as Plumier's *Plantarum*

LA NOENUPHAR ROUGE DE LA CHINE. Pierre Joseph Buc'hoz, *Collection Precieuse et Enluminée des Fleurs,* 1776-1779. (HA).

ANEMONE, engraving by Claude Aubriet. Joseph
Pitton de Tournefort, ***Elemens de Botanique,***
1694. (HA).

PAINTING by Mitsunari Tosa, ca. 1710. (HA).

Americanarum from 1755 through 1760. Blunt
has little good to say about either these engravings or the Aubriet copies on which they
were based. On a more positive note, the Cleveland collections are fortunate to have an undated original watercolor on paper by Aubriet
of the exotic ***Morina orientalis.***

Aubriet was succeeded as painter at the
Jardin des Plantes by his pupil, Madelaine
Basseport, who is not represented in the Cleveland collections. Mlle. Basseport's successor as
professor of flower painting at the Jardin was
Gerard van Spaendonck, a Dutch artist and fol-
lower of van Huysum. Van Spaendonck was a
major influence on the next generation of
French botanical artists including Pancrace
Bessa and the Redoutés. The only published
work of van Spaendonck to appear during his
lifetime is the ***Fleurs Dessinées d'après Nature*** published in 1801. Some feel that van Spaendonck's
works are at least as good as his far more cel-

MORINA ORIENTALIS, a painting by
Claude Aubriet. (HA).

GRANDE CAPUCINE engraved by A. L. N. Chaponnier after Gerard van Spaendonck. Gerard van Spaendonck,
Fleurs Dessinées d'après Nature, 1801. (HA).

ebrated successor at the Jardin, Pierre Joseph
Redouté. The ***Fleurs Dessinées***, which were engraved in stipple by Pierre François Legrand,
and printed both in color and in black, look
forward to the more celebrated flower books
of Redouté. The Holden Arboretum has an
almost complete set of the color prints and a
full set of the black prints. The latter allow
the delicacy of the stipplework to be appreciated without the distraction of the colors.

ROSE DE PROVINS or **ROSE GALLICA L.,**
engraving by Pierre François Le Grand
after Gerard van Spaendonck. Gerard
van Spaendonck, ***Fleurs Dessinées***
d'après Nature, 1801.(HA).

BEFORE DISCUSSING Pierre Joseph Redouté and the age of the elegant stipple-engraved color botanical books, it is necessary to backtrack and review some of the other seventeenth and eighteenth century works from outside of France that are in the collections.

The George Gehring Marshall Collection of Herbals at the Allen Memorial Medical Library of the Cleveland Medical Library Association contains a manuscript herbal with ink botanical sketches (some colored), entitled *Plantae ad Vivum Depictae,* which is believed to have been made in the late sixteenth or early seventeenth century. There is considerable variance in the work both in the amount of text provided for a given entry and in the completeness of the sketches.

Also in the Marshall Collection is a manuscript florilegium believed to have been produced in the vicinity of Nuremburg in the eighteenth century. The work is organized by months of the year from January through November, although there are no illustrations for October and November.

The Holden Arboretum has two quite disparate sets of botanical paintings that are believed to have been painted in Italy in the eighteenth century. The first of these bears the manuscript title of *Erbario di Numero 400 Piante Fatto per Impressione* and was written and painted at Friuli by someone describing himself as Pietro del Torre del Fu Giulio. The work has stiff symmetrical illustrations of plants with no efforts at either shading for artistic effect or detailing the flowers to provide botanical information. It is more reminiscent of the early herbals than of the work of the eighteenth century, the period to which it has been ascribed.

The second illustrated manuscript at the Arboretum is believed to be of (northern) Italian origin and bears the spine title *Herbier Colorié*. The paintings may date from as early as 1742, the date of the watermark on their paper, although the leaves of Latin text are on paper watermarked 1777. The paintings themselves are of a high quality and reminiscent of Redouté or Bessa in their treatment of the subjects.

Also at the Arboretum is a group of seven leaves with watercolors on the rectos and Latin text on the versos which are the work of Joseph von Boslarn, a professor of philosophy, who died at Amberg in 1791.

In terms of printed works, some mention should be made of the *Historia Botanica Practica* published in 1744. The work was written and illustrated by Giambattista Morandi, who was botanical artist at the botanical garden of Castello Valentino under Victor Emanuel II of Savoy. In general, the pictures are not overly impressive and feature a large number of small plant illustrations crowded together on a single

HELENIUM, an anonymous painted drawing. *Plantae ad Vivum Depictae*, late sixteenth or early seventeenth century. (CMLA).

CONVALLARIA MULTIFLORA, painting by Pietro del Torre del Fu Giulio. ***Erbario di Numero 400 Piante Fatto per Impressione***, eighteenth century. (HA).

PAINTING.
Herbier Colorié.
Italy: after 1742.
(HA).

PAPAVER, an anonymous painting. ***Florilegium***.
Nuremberg: eighteenth century. (CMLA).

Cynoglossum.   Hundßzüngs.

CYNOGLOSSUM, painting by Joseph von Boslarn. (HA).

plate. In the Cleveland copy, the effect of the plates is worsened by an indelicate hand-coloring using a green pigment which is gradually deteriorating to a brown.

A somewhat more impressive Italian work is the **Hortus Romanus** which was compiled by Giorgio Bonelli and Niccolo Martelli from specimens provided by Liberato and Constantine Sabbatin and published at Rome in eight volumes from 1772 through 1793. The large plates are engraved by Magdalen Bouchard, the daughter of one of the publishers, after original paintings by Cesare Ubertini.

The dominant botanical illustrator of the mid-eighteenth century, however, was Georg Dionysius Ehret. Ehret, who learned the rudiments of drawing as a boy from his father who was a market gardener, was apprenticed early as a garden assistant to an uncle at Bessungen in Germany. Shortly thereafter Ehret's father died and his mother remarried a man named Kesselbach who had charge of the two gardens of the Elector of Heidelberg, one of which was subsequently placed in Ehret's charge. There he attracted the attention of the Margrave of Baden, whose service he entered. The Margrave's preferential treatment of Ehret, owing to his appreciation of Ehret's floral painting, created dissension among the Margrave's other gardeners and led to Ehret's resignation.

After a period of traveling, Ehret settled at Regensburg where he was employed by Johann Wilhelm Weinmann, a pharmacist, to prepare drawings of plants to serve as originals for the plates in the **Phytanthoza-iconographia**. The relationship proved to be untenable for both parties since, when Ehret asked for payment for 500 drawings that he had produced in the course of a year, Weinmann countered by complaining that he was supposed to have produced 1000 drawings and gave Ehret less than half the amount stipulated. When the work was finally published between 1737 and 1745, no mention of Ehret, N. Asamin, or the other art-

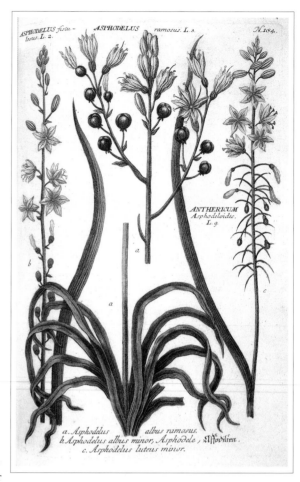

ASPHODELUS FISTULOSUS, ASPHODELUS RAMOSUS, and **ANTHERICUM ASPHODELOIDES.** Johann Wilhelm Weinmann, **Phytanthoza Iconographia,** [1737-]1745. (HA).

ists who produced the original drawings was made, although J.J. Haid, J.E. Ridinger, and J. Seuter were acknowledged as the engravers. Haid, for his part, was apparently partially paid for his engravings with copies of the work. The Cleveland collections include a variant issue dated 1745 that was sold by Haid, and another variant bearing a cancel engraved title, **Weinmannus Redivivus Emendatus et Illustratus, sive Thesaurus Rei Herbariae Locupletissimus,** dated 1787, which was sold by Haid's son after his death. The work is of interest for its use of a mezzotint ground in some of its plates to produce color printed botanical illustrations.

Weinmann's work was not, however, the first etched or engraved botanical work to be printed in colors. It was preceded by John Martyn's *Historia Plantarum Rariorum* of 1728 through 1737, and the Society of Gardeners' *Catalogus Plantarum* (composed by Philip Miller) of 1730. Both of these works had their original illustrations painted by Jacob van Huysum, the younger brother of the more celebrated Dutch flower painter, Jan van Huysum. The color printed illustrations in both were the work of Elisha Kirkall (or Kirkhall), although there is some dispute about the media used to produce the ground to hold the color. Most recently Blanche Henrey, backed by the opinion of Brian Reade in the Department of Prints and Drawings of the Victoria and Albert Museum, has held that the ground is composed of true

CASSIA BAHAMENSIS, PINNIS FOLIORUM MUCRO-NATIS, ANGUSTIS, CALYCE FLORIS NONREFLEXO, color mezzotint or pseudo-mezzotint by Elisha Kirkall after Jacob van Huysum. John Martyn, ***Historia Plantarum Rariorum,*** 1728[-1737]. (**HA**).

PINUS SYLVESTRIS, color mezzotint or pseudo-mezzotint by Elisha Kirkall after Jacob van Huysum. Philip Miller for a Society of Gardeners, ***Catalogus Plantarum,*** 1730. (**HA**).

mezzotint with the sections that appear white scraped away on the plates with a scraper. Wilfrid Blunt, on the other hand, has held that the ground is really a mock-mezzotint effect obtained by only roughening the toned parts of the plate with a roulette. Whichever process was used, the illustrations possess a unique quality unlike any of the later color work produced with aquatint or stipple.

Following his sojourn with Weinmann, Ehret worked for several years for a Regensburg banker named Leskenkohl. Much of this time was spent in copying the plates of the ***Hortus***

Malabaricus. Although the plates of the *Hortus* are handsome pieces, this was not a task for an original talent such as Ehret. Fortunately, it was during this period that Ehret came to the attention of Dr. Christoph Jakob Trew, who was to become Ehret's lifelong patron.

After quitting his job with Leskenkohl, Ehret embarked on a trip through Europe during which he engaged in botanizing and painting and made the acquaintance of Bernard de Jussieu, Sir Hans Sloane, Philip Miller, and the young Carl Linnaeus. In Holland he sold a number of paintings to George Clifford, the wealthy Anglo-Dutch banker, who then commissioned him to provide the original illustrations to accompany Linnaeus's descriptions of the plants in Clifford's garden at Hartecamp. The fruit of these labors is the handsomest of the Linnaean publications, the *Hortus Cliffortianus* of 1737 with masterful engravings by Jan Wandelaar after Ehret's originals.

In 1736, Ehret returned to England and married Susannah Kennett, who was the sister-in-law of Philip Miller, the gardener of the Chelsea physic garden. Ehret spent the rest of his life in England in a career of painting, illustrating, and teaching. Plates after Ehret are found in a wide variety of publications including Griffith Hughes's *The Natural History of Barbados* (1750), Mark Catesby's *The Natural History of Carolina, Florida, and the Bahama Islands* (which is present in the Cleveland collections in the third edition of 1771), and Alexander Russell's *The Natural History of Aleppo* (1794).

The two major collections of prints after Ehret in the Cleveland collections, however, were printed in Germany for Trew. The earlier work is the *Plantae Selectae* which was published from 1750 through 1773, with the portion completed after Trew's death in 1769 done by Benedict Christoph Vogel. The work contains illustrations of many plants then recently introduced into European gardens from America, including many species of cactus and various

tropical fruits. All of the engravings were done by Johann Jacob Haid, the same engraver who had played a prominent part in Weinmann's publication, after original paintings by Ehret in Trew's collection. The Cleveland copy is of particular interest since it includes a printed list, signed by Haid, of 240 Ehret botanical paintings that were in Trew's collection by 1750.

The second work is the *Hortus Nitidissimis Omnem per Anneum Superbiens Floribus* bearing publication dates of 1768 through 1786, but actually believed to have been produced from 1750 through 1792. The *Hortus* is essentially a florilegium of ornamental garden flowers prepared by the artists and engravers for whom Trew served as patron. The first 43 plates are engraved by Johann Michael Seligmann while 140 of the plates that follow are by Adam

CORONA IMPERIALIS II, engraving by Adam Wirsing after Georg Dionysius Ehret. Christoph Jakob Trew, *Hortus Nitidissimis Omnem per Anneum Superbiens Floribus,* [1750-]1768-1786[-1792]. (HA).

Ludwig Wirsing. Although Ehret supplied the most originals for the plates, other artists represented in the work include Barbara Regina Dietsch, Nikolaus Friedrich Eisenberger (who was court painter to the Emperor), August Wilhelm Sievert, and Johann Christoph Keller (who was professor of drawing at Erlangen University). The work has been widely celebrated for the beauty of its pictures which led Blunt to call it one of the most decorative florilegia of the mid-eighteenth century.

While the plates done after Ehret's originals are attractive and sometimes highly dramatic, they cannot convey the vitality and sensitivity of his paintings. The Cleveland collections include seven original signed paintings by Ehret, all done in his favorite media of watercolor on vellum. Three of the paintings are undated and consist of: *Corallodendron*, *The Larix with Darker Shoots of Mr. P. Collinson*, and *Viburnum*. The four dated paintings are labeled as "*Quamodit foliis tenuiter incisis & pennatis. Tourn.*" (1743), *Abies* (1744), *Yucca* (1747), and *Solanum* (1759).

CORALLODENDRON, TRYPHYLLUM-AMERICANUM SPINOSUM FLORA RUBERIMMO, painting by Georg Dionysius Ehret. (HA).

QUAMODIT FOLIIS TENNITER INCISIS PENNATIS TOURN, painting by Georg Dionysius Ehret, 1743. (GC).

Two other German artists of this period should be mentioned briefly. Georg Wolfgang Knorr was a painter, engraver, paleontologist, and art merchant who set out to prepare a large illustrated work on plants. Although Knorr had an engraved title for the work printed in 1750 and continued to produce plates for it until his death in 1761, none of the material was issued. It was only after Knorr's death that three German botanists set out to provide an accompanying text, and Knorr's *Thesaurus Rei Herbariae Hortensisque Universalis* was finally published in 1771 and 1772.

Johann Sebastian Müller, a Nuremberg artist who settled in London, is better remembered under the anglicized name of John Miller. Miller is mainly represented in the collections through the engravings he did for various gardening publications by Philip Miller. The largest body of these is found in Philip Miller's *Figures of the Most Beautiful, Useful, and Uncommon Plants Described in the Gardeners Dictionary* (1771), where John Miller did 207 of the engravings including 64 after his own original designs. Other works mainly illustrated by Miller in the collections include the 1786 and 1812 editions of John Evelyn's *Silva* and *Terra,* while three hundred and sixteen plates engraved after original pieces by John Miller are in Robert Thornton's *British Flora* published in 1812, which is somewhat puzzling since Miller had died circa 1790.

Several other illustrators of note are involved in the works produced by Nicolaus Joseph Jacquin, the Dutch born physician, botanist, and chemist. Jacquin led a varied career that included periods as professor of practical mining and chemical knowledge at the mining school at Chemnitz and as professor of botany and chemistry and director of the botanical garden at the University of Vienna. In 1754 Jacquin was appointed Imperial Botanist by Emperor Francis I, who sent Jacquin along with Richard van der Schot, the head gardener at the Schoenbrun Palace, to collect plants and animals from the West Indies and Central America. Although much of the herbarium assembled by Jacquin on this expedition was lost to ants, his watercolor sketches survived and provided the basis for the engravings in the first edition of his *Selectarum Stirpium Americanarum Historia* published in 1763. Around 1780, Jacquin prepared a deluxe edition of the work in which paintings took the place of plates. The work was limited to somewhere between 12 and 18 copies. The best part of the work is the painted floral title page which is believed to represent some of the earliest surviving work of Ferdinand Bauer. The paintings of plants are not very delicate and have generally remained unattributed.

ANONYMOUS PAINTING. Nicolaus Joseph Jacquin, *Selectarum Stirpium Americanarum Historia,* 1780. (HA).

The collection at the Holden Arboretum, however, which holds the Cleveland copy of the deluxe edition of the *Selectarum Stirpium Americanarum Historia,* also has a series of seven books of paintings which may provide a clue to its illustrators. The first four volumes in the series are composed of original watercolors and drawings by Ignaz Strenzel, Johann Baptiste Drechsler, Franz Reinelli, Johann Buchberger, Johann Schmidt, and other artists associated with the Vienna Porzellan-Manufaktur. These watercolors were exhibited in the Wiener Congress Ausstellung of 1896, and some of them were published in Leopold Trattinick's *Thesaurus Botanicus* of 1819. The fifth volume is more problematical since it contains illustrations by "Jebmayer", Schmidt, Buchberger, and Reinelli mixed with what must be copies of illustrations from *Flora Peruviana et Chilensis* by Ruiz Lopez and José Pavon which was published from 1798 through 1802. The sixth volume has paintings

NICOLAI JOSEPHI JACQUIN
SELECTARUM STIRPIUM
AMERICANARUM
HISTORIA
IN QUA
AD LINNÆANUM SYSTEMA DETERMINATÆ
DESCRIPTÆQUE SISTUNTUR PLANTÆ ILLÆ, QUAS
IN INSULIS MARTINICA, JAMAICA, DOMINGO, ALI
ISQUE, ET IN VICINÆ CONTINENTIS PARTE,
OBSERVAVIT RARIORES, ADJECTIS
ICONIBUS AD AUTORIS ARCHETYPA
PICTIS.

PAINTED TITLE PAGE attributed to Ferdinand Bauer. Nicolaus Joseph Jacquin, *Selectarum Stirpium Americanarum Historia*, 1780. (HA).

by Schmid, Grillmayer, Frister, Trittinick, and Strenzel. The seventh volume, which is anonymous, contains a series of paintings done in similar pigments and in a similar style to those found in the deluxe **Selectarum Stirpium Americanarum Historia** and are painted on paper bearing watermarks identical to those found in the Jacquin work, suggesting that the artist used by Jacquin came from this group.

Through the early 1770s, Jacquin provided most of the original art for his illustrated publications, thus we find Jacquin listed as the sole artist for his **Observationum Botanicarum Iconibus ab Auctore Delineatis Illustratarum** published from 1764 through 1771, and Jacquin and Franz Scheidl listed as providing the originals for the handsome illustrations in the **Hortus Botanicus Vindobonensis** published from 1770 through 1776. In the **Florae Austriacae . . . Icones** of 1773 through 1778, Jacquin ceased to provide the originals for the illustrations and left the task primarily to Franz Scheidl with some illustrations apparently also provided by Franz Xavier Wulfen.

The most celebrated of the Jacquin influenced illustrators are the Bauer brothers,

DIPSACU LACINIATIIS, anonymous painting from the volumes associated with the Vienna Porzellan-Manufaktur group. **(HA).**

Ferdinand and Francis (or Franz). The Bauers, born in Feldsberg, Austria, were the sons of the botanical artist to the Prince of Liechtenstein. Their father died when they were in their infancy, leaving their mother to train them in the art of botanical illustration. By the time that they were in their twenties, both brothers were in Jacquin's employ where they combined their talents with Joseph Hofbauer and Johann Scharf to provide the originals for the engravings by Jakob Adams in Jacquin's **Icones Plantarum Rariorum** published from 1781 through 1795.

As we have already mentioned, Jacquin introduced Ferdinand Bauer to John Sibthorp in 1784, and Ferdinand subsequently accepted the position of botanical illustrator on Sibthorp's first expedition to the Levant, from which they returned to Oxford in 1787. There Ferdinand worked on the originals for the plates of the **Flora Graeca**. In 1800, Ferdinand joined the ill-fated Matthew Flinders expedition to Australia as botanical artist, returning to England some five years later. Eventually he returned to Austria where he retired. Apart from the works already cited, Ferdinand is represented in the Cleveland collections by plates after his originals in the second edition of Aylmer Bourke Lambert's **A Description of the Genus Pinus** (1828-1829; first edition 1803-1824) and in the first edition of John Lindley's **Digitalium Monographia** published in 1821.

Francis Bauer came to visit his brother Ferdinand in England and remained there the rest of his life. Through the generosity of Sir Joseph Banks and with the approval of the King of England, Francis was given the position of botanical artist at Kew Gardens, where he settled in 1790. The chief example of his work in Cleveland is in his rare **Delineations of Exotick Plants Cultivated at Kew** published from 1796 to 1803 (but with plates dated as early as 1793). The hand-colored plates engraved by D. MacKenzie depict specimens of heaths grown at Kew from the specimens collected at the Cape of Good Hope by Francis Masson. Their beauty and detail display the qualities which led Blunt to call Francis Bauer the greatest botanical artist of all time.

ERICA SEBAMA, engraving by D. Mackenzie after Francis Bauer. Francis Bauer, *Delineations of Exotick Plants Cultivated in the Royal Garden at Kew,* 1796[-1803]. (HA).

*T*O RETURN TO FRANCE and the mid-eighteenth century, one must take note of *La Botanique Mise à la Portée de Tout le Monde,* dated 1774 but actually published between 1770 and 1780. Blunt termed this work the most impressive French botanical work of the period. The book was written by Nicolas François Regnault, a French physician and engraver, who combined with his wife, Genevieve de Nangis Regnault, to provide the original art and subsequent engravings for the work.

Both Pierre Joseph Redouté, who is generally considered the greatest floral artist of all time, and James Sowerby, who was the most prolific English botanical illustrator of his time, make their first published appearances in the works of Charles Louis L'Héritier de Brutelle. L'Héritier was a French juror and amateur botanist who served as superintendent of waters and forests for the Paris region, councillor (judge) of the Cour des Aides (an ancient financial court), a commander of his district battalion of the National Guard, and a *commis* in the Ministry of Justice after the French Revolution. He eventually became chief secretary of the ministry as well as a judge in the Tribunal d'Appel. He was also a member of the Commission d'Agriculture et des Arts.

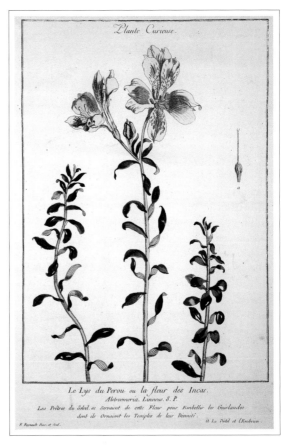

LE LYS DE PERU OU LA FLEUR DES INCAS, hand-finished color engraving by Nicolaus François Regnault. Nicolaus François Regnault and Genevieve Nangis de Regnault, *La Botanique Mise à la Portée de Tout le Monde,* [1770-]1774[-1780]. (HA).

Pierre Joseph Redouté was born in the town of St. Hubert in what is currently Belgium. His father and grandfather were both painters and interior decorators. Pierre began his career as an itinerant painter at the age of 13. In 1782, he joined his elder brother, Antoine Ferdinand, in Paris where they designed scenery for the Théâtre Italien. Pierre's main interest, however, was flower painting. This brought him to the Jardin des Plantes where he came under the artistic influence of Gerard van Spaendonck and the scientific influence of L'Héritier.

L'Héritier's first publication was the **Stirpes Novae,** bearing a publication date of 1784 but actually published from 1785 through 1791. As the title indicates, the work focused on new plants. The early engravings were after originals by Louis Freret, but engravings after the

PODOCARPUS ELONGATA, "unpublished engraved plate" by François Hubert after James Sowerby intended for the continuation of Charles Louis L'Héritier de Brutelle's **Stirpes Novae.** (HA).

young P. J. Redouté begin appearing with the second fascicle and account for the majority of illustrations in the work. As is the case with most of L'Héritier's publications, the work was never completed owing to a combination of occasional financial problems and the chaotic situation brought on by the French Revolution. The Cleveland collections include a number of so-called unpublished plates which were apparently intended for a continuation of the **Stirpes Novae**. These consist of **Oxybaphus viscosus** and **Podocarpus elongata**, after originals by James Sowerby, and **Broussonetia papyrifera** and **Hemitomus triphyllus**, after originals by P. J. Redouté. It is possible that these plates were also intended to illustrate the rare "monographies" that consisted of a plate and a few leaves of text, which L'Héritier is known to have produced in extremely limited quantities for distribution among his friends. This possibility is suggested further by the fact that L'Héritier is known to have given papers (apparently unpublished) before the Academy of Sciences on *Hemitomus* and *Podocarpus* in 1791. The monographies are definitely represented in Cleveland by that on **Hymenopappus**, believed to have been published circa 1788, which features another plate engraved after a Redouté original.

In looking for new plants to feature in his **Stirpes Novae**, L'Héritier became interested in the herbarium of plants from Chile and Peru that Joseph Dombey had assembled from the joint French-Spanish expedition ostensibly led by Ruiz Lopez and Pavon. After returning from Peru and Chile in 1785, Dombey had agreed to the demands of the Spanish government that he would not publish anything on his travels or the discoveries of the expedition until Ruiz Lopez and Pavon had returned to Spain. In exchange for his cooperation, he was allowed to retain the French part of the herbarium. Being in financial straits and unable to do anything with the collection, Dombey negotiated

BROUSSONETIA PAPYRIFERA, "unpublished plate" by Milsan after Pierre Joseph Redouté. (HA).

tance of James Sowerby, who after studying at the Royal Academy Schools and articling (a kind of apprenticeship) under the marine painter, Richard Wright, had begun earning a living by teaching, drawing, and painting portraits. James Sowerby was to go on to become the foremost English illustrator of works on natural history of his period and the progenitor of a line of illustrators of natural history.

P. J. Redouté, whom L'Héritier had summoned to England from France, and James Sowerby provided all but three of the illustrations for L'Héritier's next major publication, the **Sertum Anglicum** that bears a publication date of 1788 but was actually issued from 1789 through 1792, which celebrates the plants L'Héritier had studied in England. It features engravings after the original drawings, which were all made in England, and the dedication of a number of new genera to various figures associated with English botany.

the sale of the herbarium with Georges-Louis Leclerc, Comte de Buffon, the director of the Jardin du Roi (later called the Jardin des Plantes and Muséum d'Histoire Naturelle), in return for a grant in aid and a state pension. Buffon, in turn, gave custody of the herbarium to L'Héritier who offered to publish the material from it at his own expense. The Spanish government, on learning of L'Héritier's plans, demanded that France return the material to Spain, and Buffon was ordered to comply with this request. Before Buffon was able to comply with this order, however, L'Héritier spirited the collection across the channel to England.

L'Héritier stayed nearly 15 months in England, where he appears to have spent more time examining the rare plants in Sir Joseph Banks's herbarium and those growing at Kew than in working on the specimens in the Dombey herbarium. While in England, he made the acquain-

HEMITOMUS TRYPHYLLUS, "unpublished plate" by Stephen Voysard after Pierre Joseph Redouté. (HA).

L'Héritier's *Geraniologia* of 1787 through 1788 (with the last plates dating to 1791) featured the majority of plates engraved after P. J. Redouté, six plates after Sowerby, and one plate after P. J. Redouté's brother, Henri Joseph Redouté. The slender volume of L'Héritier's *Cornus*, the first monograph on dogwoods, which bears a publication date of 1788 but was actually published in 1798, has the originals for the plates evenly divided between Louis Freret and P. J. Redouté. In addition to these works, L'Héritier also asked P. J. Redouté to do a series of original drawings of succulent plants. Although never used by L'Héritier, these formed the basis for the color stipple engravings in Auguste Pyramus de Candolle's *Plantarum Succulentarum Historia* published from 1799 to about 1805. It was the first book entirely illustrated by Redouté using this process.

Stipple engraving is actually an etching process in which the image and its shadings and gradations are produced by a series of dots and the amount of white space left between them. The dots are made on a ground using a graver and then etched into the plate. According to Blunt, the process was developed in France in the eighteenth century, but it was popularized by W. W. Ryland and Francesco Bartolozzi in England, which is where Redouté is believed to have learned about it. He had, however, previously learned about color engraving from Gilles-Antoine Demarteau. Redouté claimed to have invented the use of stipple engraving for printing multiple colors on a single plate in 1796. His claim was upheld in the French courts and Louis XVIII awarded him a medal for the invention. Whatever its origins, color stipple engraving reached its height in the French botanical and floral works, especially in those in which Redouté was involved.

Redouté's career continued to prosper with his appointment to the prestigious, although little used, position of draftsman and painter to the cabinet of Queen Marie Antoinette.

MESEMBRYANTHEMUM filamentosum FICOIDE filamenteux.
H.J.Redouté.Pinx.

MESEMBRYANTHEUM FILAMENTOSUM, color engraving by Pierre Joseph Redouté after Henri Joseph Redouté. Augustin Pyramus de Candolle, ***Plantarum Succulentarum Historia,*** 1799[-1805]. (GC).

Somewhat more rewarding was the appointment of both Pierre Joseph Redouté and his brother Henri Joseph Redouté to the staff of the Muséum at the Jardin des Plantes in 1793. P. J. Redouté's work of the 1790's is represented in Cleveland by the engravings after his originals found in two local floras. Philippe Isadore Picot de Lapeyrouse's *Figures de la Flore des Pyrénées* (1795 to 1801) features color stipple plates, mainly of saxifrages, engraved by F. Durrisseau principally after originals by Laferrerie, but including 11 plates after Redouté. Réné Louiche Desfontaines's *Flora Atlantica* is a flora of North-West Africa published in 1798 which features plates mainly engraved by Sellier, including 106 after originals by Marechal, 88 after P. J. Redouté, and 58 after H. J. Redouté.

Although P. J. Redouté is normally thought of as a flower painter, he also did illustrations for several works where the same delicacy found in his treatment of flowers is applied to the foliage and fruits of trees and shrubs. Perhaps the most famous of these is the celebrated *Nouveau Duhamel*, so-called because it purports to be a second edition of Henri Louis Duhamel du Monceau's *Traité des Arbres et Arbustes*. It is actually an entirely new work on the subject with text supplied by C.F. Mirbel, J. Loiseleur-Deslongchamps, J.H. Jaume Saint-Hilaire, E. Michel, and L. Poiret. The work was published between 1800 and 1819 and features stipple engravings which appear to be hand colored in the Cleveland copies. The illustrations include 304 plates after P. J. Redouté and 186 after Pancrace Bessa.

Tome I. Pl. 58.

WOODCUT FIRST USED by Mattioli reused in Henri Louis Duhamel's *Traité des Arbres et Arbustes,* 1755. (HA).

CRATEAGUS TORMINALIS, color engraving by Gabriel after Pierre Joseph Redouté. Henri Louis Duhamel du Monceau, *Traité des Arbres et Arbustes,* [1800-]1804-1819. (HA).

Only slightly less famous is a series of works on American trees done by father and son André and François André Michaux. The first of these present in Cleveland is the *Histoire des Chênes de l'Amérique* (1801) featuring stipple engravings after both P. J. and H. J. Redouté. Later works by François André Michaux in Cleveland are the *Histoire de Pins et des Sapins de l'Amérique Septentrionale* (1810), the *Histoire des Arbres Forestiers de l'Amérique Septentrionale* (1810 to 1813), and the *North American Sylva* (1819). Most of the plates in these works are after originals by Pancrace Bessa, but they also have plates after both P. J. and H. J. Redouté. The latter two works also have two plates signed after A. Redouté, the A. standing for Adelaide, P. J. Redouté's daughter who died in 1822.

Cleveland has both the quarto and folio editions of Jean Jacques Rousseau's *La Botanique* which was issued with plates after P. J. Redouté in 1805. Etienne Pierre Ventenat's

Choix des Plantes dont la Plupart sont Cultivées dans le Jardin de Cels featured stipple plates engraved mainly by Sellier after four of the preeminent botanical artists of the time: P. J. Redouté, P. J. F. Turpin, Pancrace Bessa, and Antoine Poiteau.

In the meantime, Pierre Joseph Redouté had acquired his most important patron in the person of the Empress Josephine who engaged him as her painter after her accession in 1804. Among the works which enjoyed her patronage are some of Redouté's finest, including the massive *Les Liliacées* published from 1802 to

IXIA TRICOLOR, color engraving by Langlois after Pierre Joseph Redouté. Pierre Joseph Redouté, *Les Liliacées*, 1802-1816. (HA).

1816. The Cleveland collection also boasts a copy of Aimé Bonpland's *Descriptions des Plantes Rares Cultivées a Malmaison et a Navarre*, which is dated 1813 but was actually published from 1811 to 1817. Although published after Josephine had lost her imperial status by divorce, the magnificence of the plants and gar-

dens she had assembled are celebrated in the latter work by the color plates after P. J. Redouté and Pancrace Bessa, which Gordon Dunthorne[5] believed to be the finest of the Redouté illustrations. Four of the original illustrations for this work, an undated *Duvalia oxalidofia*, an 1813 *Bossoiea coccinea*, an 1814 *Dalea mutabilis*, and an 1816 *Dalea bicolor,* are at the Holden Arboretum.

The most celebrated of Pierre Joseph Redouté's works is *Les Roses*, which was published with text by Claude Antoine Thory from 1817 through 1824. The copy at the Cleveland Botanical Garden is one of the five (or fifteen according to some authors) special large copies that features not only the color plates but black plates as well. This copy is of even greater importance, since it also contains original signed paintings by P. J. Redouté of *Rosier pimprenelle* (May 24, 1822) and *Rosier spinulé de Dalmatia* (May 6, 1822).

ROSA GALLICA VERSICOLOR, color engraving by Langlois after Pierre Joseph Redouté. Pierre Joseph Redouté and Charles Antoine Thory, *Les Roses*, 1817-1824. (GC).

[5]Gordon Dunthorne is a specialist in 18th century botanical illustration. References are to: Dunthorne, Gordon. Flower and Fruit Prints of the 18th and Early 19th Centuries. Washington, D.C.: the author, 1938.

ROSIER PIMPRENELLE, painting by Pierre Joseph Redouté. May 24, 1822. (GC).

Also at the Holden Arboretum are two original paintings by Redouté of *Stapelia* and of a wild rose.

STAPELIA, painting by Pierre Joseph Redouté. (HA).

Pancrace Bessa, whom we have already had occasion to mention several times, is generally regarded as a pupil of van Spaendonck and P. J. Redouté. His chief patron was the Duchess de Berry, whom he instructed in painting. Among the works in Cleveland illustrated by Bessa is Charles Malo's *Histoire des Tulipes*, a sentimental flower book believed to have been published circa 1821. The single largest source of illustrations engraved after Bessa originals, however, is the *Herbier Général de l'Amateur* of Jean Claude Michel Mordant de Launay and Jean Louis Auguste Loiseleur-Deslongchamps published from 1810 through 1827, and the reworked version by Pierre Auguste Joseph Drapiez published as *Herbier de l'Amateur de Fleurs* (1828 through 1835). The Holden Arboretum also has a manuscript version of the first 72 entries of the *Herbier Général* arranged in a different

order and accompanied by unsigned watercolors that are probably by Bessa. In addition there are six signed, but undated and unlabeled, Bessa watercolors on vellum at the Arboretum. These appear to be pictures of an iris, a Turk's head lily, a blue daisy, a magnolia, a stewartia, and a laurel.

Two other illustrators in the grand botanical tradition of French illustration are Pierre Jean François Turpin and Pierre-Antoine Poiteau. Turpin, whom Blunt terms "possibly the greatest natural genius of all the French botanical painters of his day," was trained at the art school at Vire. As a member of the batallion du Calvados, he was sent to Santo Domingo, where he met Poiteau. Poiteau, who was a self-taught botanist, had worked as a gardener at the Jardin des Plantes and had been sent by Thouin to found the botanical garden at Bergerac before being sent to Santo Domingo. He later served as gardener in charge of the nursery at Versailles. The two went on to illus-

AMARYLLIS CRISPA, painting attributed to Pancrace Bessa. Jean Claude Michel Mordaunt de Launay, manuscript of *Herbier Général de l'Amateur,* 1810. (HA).

trate some of the most important scientific works of the period - most notably the *Plantes Equinoxiales*, published from 1805 through 1817, and the *Monographie des Melastomacées*, published from 1806 to 1816, both of which comprised part of the botanical researches resulting from the expedition of Humboldt and Bonpland. Turpin and Poiteau also provided the originals for the illustrations in Augustin Pyramus de Candolle's *Icones Plantarum Galliae Rariorum* (1808). They joined with P. J. Redouté to provide the originals for the plates in François Richard Tussac's *Flore des Antilles* published from 1808 to 1828.

lustrations of François Pierre Chaumeton, Jean Chamberet, and Turpin's *Flore Médicale* published from 1814 through 1820. In addition, the Holden Arboretum has an 1814 manuscript version of the work. The illustrations are unsigned, but if original, they are paintings by Turpin and Pancoucke.

Turpin also combined with Eulalia Delile to provide the originals for the plates of Auguste de Saint-Hilaire, Adrien Henri Laurent de Jussieu, and Jacques Cambessèdes's *Flora Brasiliae Meridionalis* published from 1825 through 1832.

MELASTOMA CILIATA, color engraving by Louis Bouquet after Pierre Jean François Turpin. Alexander Friedrich von Humboldt and Aimé Bonpland, *Monographie des Melastomacées,*

Turpin and Poiteau also worked independently. In the Cleveland collections, we find Turpin combining with Mme. Ernestine Pancoucke to provide the originals for the il-

CAROTTE, painting by Pierre Jean François Turpin. François Pierre Chaumeton, Jean Chambert, and Pierre Jean François Turpin, manuscript of *Flore Medicale,* 1814. (HA).

Poiteau is also represented in the Cleveland collections in the sumptuous stipple engravings of fruit after his original designs in the *Histoire Naturelle des Orangers* (1818) that he and Antoine Risso compiled.

Jean Henri Jaume Saint-Hilaire, who studied botany and floral painting at the Muséum d'Histoire Naturelle (the latter under van Spaendonck), is represented in Cleveland by his *Plantes de la France* ([1805-]1808-1809) and *La Flore et la Pomone Françaises* (1828[-1835]).

ASTER À GRANDES FLEURS.

Other French botanical artists represented in the Cleveland collections include J. Grasset de Saint-Sauveur, who engraved and colored the plates for Joseph Roques' *Plantes Usuelles Indigènes et Exotiques* (1807-1808); Alexander Louis Marquis, whose delicate engravings after his own originals grace Jean Louis Auguste Loiseleur-Deslongchamps's *Flora Gallica* (1806-1807); A. Vigneux, who illustrated his own *Flore Pittoresque des Environs de Paris* (1812);

Hocquart, who did the engravings after his own originals for Joseph Roques' *Phytographie Médicale* (1821-1825); and M. J. Th. Descourtilz, who did the original artwork for Michel Etienne Descourtilz's *Flore Pittoresque et Médicale des Antilles* ([1821-]1827-1833).

Jean-Louis Prevost is represented in the collections through the renderings of his originals in the delicate color stipple engravings of L. C. Ruotte in Prevost's *Collection des Fleurs et des Fruits Peints d'après Nature* ([1804-]1805[-1806]), a florilegium designed for decorative artists. The special quality of Prevost's work is also demonstrated in the original floral painting of *Delphinium ajacis* done for the same work, which is at the Holden Arboretum.

Emblemes et Devises (1821) is also at the Arboretum. It is a delicate, predominantly floral, emblem book hand-written and painted by Stéphanie Félicité Ducrest, Countess of Genlis (otherwise known as Mme. Genlis).

The post-Ehret German illustrations in the collections are generally unimpressive. One must note, however, the neat but modest engravings with full botanical detail of Jacob Sturm and his son, Johann Wilhelm Sturm, in their *Deutschlands Flora* published from 1798 through 1855.

Of more interest is the German-born Jean Christoph Heyland whose original Christian name was Kumpfler. He was apprenticed at the age of twelve to his uncle, a well-known Geneva hairdresser, whose last name Jean Christoph adopted. Heyland began his artistic career making sketches for theatrical costumes, but with the support and patronage of Auguste Pyramus de Candolle, he became one of the foremost botanical illustrators of his time. The Cleveland collections boast the magnificent color stipple engravings after his work in de Candolle's *Plantes Rares du Jardin de Genève* (1825-1829). Later Heyland left Geneva to become botanical painter at the court of the Archduke Rainier, the Austrian Viceroy in Lombardy.

COLOR ENGRAVING by L. C. Ruotte after Jean Louis Prevost. Jean Louis Prevost,
Collection des Fleurs et des Fruits Peints d'après Nature, [1804-]1805[-1806]. (HA).

DELPHINIUM AJACIS, painting by Jean Louis Prevost. (HA).

ANANAS, painting by Stephanie Félicité
Ducrest, Countess of Genliss. Stephanie
Félicité Ducrest, Countess of Genliss,
Emblemes et Devises, 1821. (HA).

ers, with the former featuring plates after original drawings by Cavanilles and the latter featuring plates after Isador Galvez. Galvez was
one of the two original draftsmen on the Ruiz-
Pavon-Dombey expedition.

PAINTING by Jean Christoph Heyland.
(HA).

Heyland spent ten years in Monza, near Milan,
painting the plants of the Archduke's gardens
and greenhouses. Although owing to the for-
tunes of politics, none of Heyland's Monza
work was ever published, 122 impressive paintings (many of succulents) from this period are
currently in the collection at the Holden Arboretum.

The Spanish school of botanical illustration during the late eighteenth and early nineteenth centuries is represented by Antonio José
Cavanilles's *Icones et Descriptiones Plantarum,
Quae aut Sponte in Hispania Crescunt* (1791-
1801), Hipolito Ruiz Lopez and José Pavon's
Florae Peruvianae, et Chilensis, Prodromus (1794),
and *Flora Peruviana et Chilensis* (1798-1802[-
1807?]). The *Icones* and *Prodromus* both feature engravings by Tomas Lopez Enguidanos,
Vincent Lopez Enguidanos, and various oth-

E HAVE ALREADY
mentioned the Ruiz-Pavon-Dombey expedition to Chile and Peru in connection with
L'Héritier's flight to England with the Dombey
herbarium and the circumstances that brought
Redouté to England and ultimately led to the
publication of the *Sertum Anglicum*. Because of
the special nature of the Cleveland copy of the
Flora Peruviana et Chilensis, a few more details
of the expedition are in order at this point.

The original expedition was accompanied
by Isador (or Isadro) Galvez and Joseph

Brunete as botanical draftsmen. Although Dombey left the expedition in 1784, Ruiz and Pavon did not return to Spain until 1788. Upon their departure, the explorations were continued by Tafalla as botanist and Francesco Pulgar as botanical illustrator. Pulgar soon quit to go into business and was succeeded by José Rivera.

It was not until three years after their return to Spain that Ruiz and Pavon began meeting to publish the results of their expedition. When the *Prodromus* finally appeared in 1794, it introduced 136 new genera. Some of these, unfortunately, used names such as Ruizia, Dombeyana, and Pavonia, which Cavanilles had already used in his *Icones*. By this time, Cavanilles had succeeded Gomez Ortega (who had picked Ruiz and Pavon for the expedition) as head of the royal botanical garden in Madrid. The third volumes of his *Icones* was about to be published (1795), and he used it to attack Ruiz and Pavon's genera, resulting in a mutual antagonism.

The first volume of the *Flora Peruviana et Chilensis* finally appeared in 1798, and was followed by the second volume in 1799 and the third in 1802. In all, the first three volumes contained 325 engraved plates after originals by Isador Galvez, Francesco Pulgar, Joseph Brunete, José Rubio, José Rivera, and various combinations of the aforementioned artists. Although the project continued until Pavon was finally removed under allegations of malfeasance in 1831, no more text was to be published during the lifetimes of the expedition members. The plates for illustrations continued to be made, however, and copies of the plates pulled. Pritzel[6] and the *Catalogue of the Library of the Arnold Arboretum* both indicate that some copies of volume 3 contain plates 326-425 intended for volumes 4 and 5. The Holden Arboretum set, however, which was originally obtained from Pavon by A.B. Lambert, has the manuscript preface for the then unpublished fourth volume and a fifth volume containing

ANNONA RHOMBI PETALA, "unpublished plate" engraved by Faust Martinez Torre after Francesco Pulgar for Hipolito Ruiz Lopez and José Tavon's *Flora Peruviana Chilensis,* 1798-1807. (HA).

plates numbered 426-449, 451-490, 493-495, 503-505, 512, 515, and 538, which include plates after Xavier Cortés beginning with plate 341. It also includes two unnumbered plates of *Auracaria imbricata* (one hand-colored and one in black) engraved by V. P. Perez after an original by A. Delgado Meneses.

Italian illustration during the period is represented by a series of 122 watercolor paintings bound in four volumes and bearing the manuscript title *Plantes Plus Rares Fleuries dans le Jardin de Monsieur l'Avocat Colla Peinte d'après Nature* and the date 1819. The paintings are all by Tecophile Colla (later Colla-Billotti) and portray plants found in her father's garden. They include ten paintings which are believed to be the originals for plates found in Luigi Colla's *Hortus Ripulensis* (1824).

The collections include among their material from the Netherlands, twelve watercolor

[6]Pritzel, G.A., *Thesaurus Literaturae Botanicae.* New rev. ed., Leipzig: F. A. Brockhaus, 1872; Tucker, Ethelyn Maria, compiled under the direction of Charles Sprague Sargent and Oakes Ames, *Catalogue of the Library of the Arnold Arboretum of Harvard University.* 3 vols. Cambridge, MA: Cosmos Press, 1915-1933.

IRIS, painting and text by Tecophile Colla.
Tecophile Colla, manuscript *Plantes Plus
Rares Fleuries dans le Jardin de Monsieur
l'Avocat Colla Peint d'après Nature*, 1819.
(HA).

HAND-COLORED PLATE by Nicolaas Meerburgh.
Nicolaas Meerburgh, *Plantae rariores vivis
coloribus depictae*, 1789. (HA).

ENGRAVING after Georg Jacob van Os. Jan
Kops, *Flora Batava*, [1800-]1807-1849.
(HA).

paintings from the school of van Huysum
(fraudulently signed as van Huysum). Among
the printed material is George Voorhelm
Schneevoogt's *Icones Plantarum Rariorum*
([1792-]1793[-1795]), with plates engraved
by Hendrik Schwegman after his own designs
and those of P. van Loo, which Blunt considers
the finest of the Dutch illustrated works of the
period. Other notable Dutch works in the
Cleveland collections include Nicolaas
Meerburgh's *Plantae Rariores Vivis Coloribus
Depictae* (1789) and *Plantarum Selectarum Icones
Pictae* (1798), both of which feature original
plates by Meerburgh. Also present are the first
ten volumes of Jan Kops' *Flora Batava* ([1800-
]1807-1836). These were all the volumes supervised by Kops and have plates after the originals of Georg Jacob Johann van Os and Cornelis
Johannes van Hulstyn.

I T IS TIME TO RETURN to the English illustrators and James Sowerby, whom we last mentioned in connection with his initial botanical work for L'Héritier. Sowerby's second major patron was William Curtis.

Although Curtis always had an interest in botany and natural history, he began his career as a pharmacist. After selling his pharmaceutical practice, he began a British botanical garden in Bermondsey. As his reputation grew, he came to be appointed Praefectus Horti and Demonstrator of Plants to the Society of Apothecaries at Chelsea, the same post once held by Philip Miller. In 1777, Curtis left the Chelsea post to set up the London Botanic Garden in Lambeth. In 1789, Curtis moved his botanic garden to Brompton where he also started a nursery. Along the way, he wrote, lectured, and published extensively on botany and horticulture.

Curtis's first major publication was the *Flora Londinensis* published from 1775 to 1798. The work intended to portray and describe all the plant life growing wild within a ten mile radius of London. Unfortunately, laudible as this ambition was from a botanical point of view, it left something to be desired for a public more interested in illustrations of exotic and ornamental plants than in pictures of common plants and what, to a non-botanist, would be considered weeds. As a consequence the work was never completed. The *Flora's* original artist was William Kilburn, an Irish designer who specialized in calicoes, but who had also made drawings and engravings of flowers for print shops. He appears to have remained with the project for about three years, after which he returned to fabrics and eventually became the most eminent calico printer in England. Kilburn was succeeded on the project by James Sowerby and Sydenham Edwards, while all of the engravings were done by Francis Sansom.

Having found that the wild plants of England would not provide a wide enough market for book sales, Curtis turned his attention to providing illustrations of what he viewed as the most ornamental foreign plants raised in gardens, greenhouses, or stoves (as heated greenhouses were called) in the *Botanical Magazine*, although the plants illustrated during Curtis's tenure are often rather commonplace. The magazine, founded in 1787, is one of the longest running periodicals and continues to be published today. James Sowerby provided most of the originals for the earliest plates, but as he became more and more involved in other projects, he gave way to Sydenham Teast Edwards as the main illustrator.

ZINNIA MULTIFLORA, hand-colored engraving by Sydenham Edwards (1791). William Curtis, *Botanical Magazine*, 1787 to the present. (HA).

Edwards first came to the attention of Curtis as a young man when Curtis was shown copies he had made from plates of the *Flora Londinensis.* Curtis was sufficiently impressed that he had Edwards brought from Wales to London to be trained as an artist. Edwards was to remain the principal artist through Curtis's lifetime and continued as such until 1815, when he left as the result of a dispute to found the rival *The Botanical Register*. The main engravers for the plates during this period were Francis Sansom and, after he lost his sight, Francis Sansom, Jr. The other main contributing artists through 1829 were John Curtis, the entomologist, William Jackson Hooker, Rev. Landsdown Guilding, and William Herbert; the other engravers included H. Weddell, Joseph Swan, and Sydenham Edwards.

Sydenham Edwards and Sansom also provided the illustrations for Curtis's *Lectures on Botany* published from 1803 to 1804 and for the third edition of Colin Milne's *A Botanical*

RHODODENDRON DAURICUM, hand-colored engraving by Smith after Sydenham Edwards. *The Botanical Register*, 1829-1847. (HA).

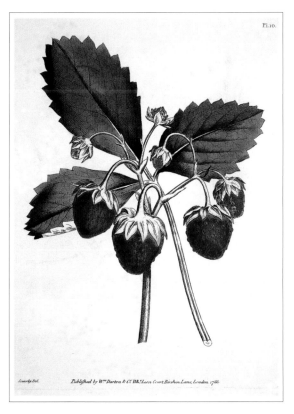

STRAWBERRIES, hand-colored engraving by James Sowerby. *The Pomona Britanica*, 1788. (HA).

Dictionary published in 1805. Nissen indicates that Sydenham Edwards is also responsible for the illustrations in the 1812 edition of Sir John Hill's *Family Herbal*.

Cleveland has a possibly unique copy of *The Pomona Britanica* of 1788, which features ten instead of the normal eight plates by James Sowerby. This copy of the unfinished work apparently was passed down in the Sowerby family since it has the engraved bookplate of W. Sowerby on the inside front cover and the manuscript inscription of Sowerby's Museum on the title page.

In 1790, Sowerby began the publication of his *English Botany*, which continued to 1814. The work featured illustrated plates by Sowerby or his son, James De Carle Sowerby, after their own illustrations, and text by James Edward Smith. Smith and Sowerby also collaborated on Smith's never-to-be-completed *Icones Pictae Plantarum Rariorum* (1790 to 1793). Interestingly, Sowerby also collaborated with Smith's frequent antagonist and proponent of the Jussieu natural system of classification, Richard Anthony Salisbury, to provide the illustrations for his *Icones Stirpium Rariorum Descriptionibus Illustratae* published in 1791.

James Sowerby is also represented in the Cleveland collections by his illustrations for the second edition of J. E. Smith's *An Introduction to Physiological and Systematical Botany* of 1809, his engravings after Bauer for Sibthorp's *Flora Graeca*, and his illustrations for William Woodville's *Medical Botany* first published from 1790 to 1795.

The success of Curtis's *Botanical Magazine* led to a steady stream of rival illustrated botanical and horticultural periodicals. The earliest of these was the *Botanist's Repository* featuring original plates by Henry C. Andrews and

ERICA MAMMOSA MINOR, color engraving by Henry Andrews. Henry Andrews, *Coloured Engravings of Heaths*, [1793-] 1802-1809. (HA).

text by John Kennedy, a nurseryman and Andrews's father-in-law. The work, published between 1797 and 1814, portrayed numerous new introductions to England, many of them available at a nursery owned by Kennedy and James Lee the Younger in Hammersmith. One group of popular plants of the time were the heaths from South Africa. These were celebrated by Andrews in a separate publication, *Coloured Engravings of Heaths,* issued from 1802 to 1809 but with plates marked as early as 1793. Less successful was Andrews's *Roses* of 1805 and 1828 which,

ROSA PROVINCIALIS REGALIS, engraving by Henry Andrews. Henry Andrews, *Roses*, 1805; 1828. (HA).

while much valued today, has often been criticized for overstylization.

Sydenham Edwards, after his break from Curtis's heirs at the *Botanical Magazine*, set up his own magazine devoted to exotic plants grown in British gardens. It was entitled *The Botanical Register* and was published from 1815 to 1847. Although Edwards's name continued to be prominently displayed on the journal's title page well after his death in 1819, the majority of plates were after originals by a mysterious M. Hart. The next largest number were after Edwards, and some of the later plates after John Lindley. The majority of the plates were engraved by J. Watts with lesser numbers by an unidentified Smith and W. J. White. The early text was supplied by J. B. Ker-Gawler with the later text by John Lindley.

Slightly later was *The Botanical Cabinet* of Conrad Loddiges and Sons, a family of gardeners of German origin who maintained a nursery in Hackney which specialized in exotic plants such as palms, camellias, and orchids, all of which figured prominently in the work. The illustrations featured engravings by George Cooke with the largest quantity after originals by Conrad Loddiges, followed closely by originals by Cooke, a substantial number after those of Thomas Shotter Boys, and the remainder after originals by various other members of the Loddiges family.

Benjamin Maund's *The Botanic Garden*, which bears publication dates from 1825 through 1826 but which is generally believed to have been published through 1851, features engraved plates containing four plants each. In the so-called "royal edition" the original plates were masked in the printing so that only one plant appears on each plate surrounded by an engraved frame with a crown at the top (the

CAMPANULA SPECIALA, engraving by S. Watts after Edward Dalton Smith. Benjamin Maund, *The Botanic Garden*, 1830's. (HA)

source of the "royal") and a fountain at the bottom. All of the signed plates are engraved by S. Watts. The majority of the plates are after originals by Edwin Dalton Smith, with others mainly after R. Mills, Miss S. Maund, and Eliza Maund.

Edwin Dalton Smith was the son of the noted engraver and miniaturist Anker Smith. He specialized mainly in flowers and provided the original artwork for the illustrations in a number of works by Robert Sweet including the *Geraniaceae* published from 1820 to 1830 (engravings by S. Watts), *The British Flower Garden* published from 1823 to 1829 (engravings by Weddell and A. Bailey), *Flora Australasica* published from 1827 to 1828 (engravings by S. Watts), and *The Florist's Guide, and Cultivator's Directory* published from 1827 to 1832 (engravings by J. Watts, one after a drawing by William Prest).

Other detailed botanical illustrations in the collections include the plates engraved by S. Watts after the author's originals in John Lindley's *Rosarum monographia* of 1820 and the engravings after originals by the author and Robert Kaye Greville in Sir William Jackson Hooker's *Exotic Flora* of 1822 to 1827. Based upon the samples in the unique copy of the

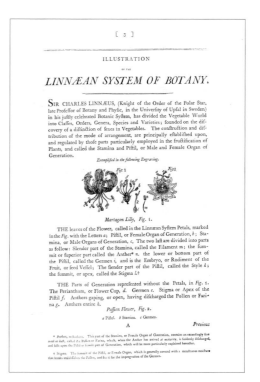

prospectus at the Holden Arboretum of the otherwise unpublished *The British Flora*, detailed treatment was also intended for the illustrations created by David Martin, the Sheffield engraver, who was author, artist, and publisher of the proposed work.

Two fructological works deserve mention. The rare *A Collection of Fruits from the West Indies* published in 1800 features hand-colored engravings with aquatint by its author, Lydia Byam, who was the elder sister of William Gunthorpe, Governor of Antigua. Thomas Andrew Knight, the English pomologist, vegetable physiologist, horticulturist, and live-stock breeder who served as president of the Horticultural Society from 1811 until his death in 1838, is represented by his *Pomona Herefordiensis*. Based upon the watermarks this copy appears to be an 1820 reissue of the 1811 work, with engravings by William Hooker (not to be confused with Sir William Jackson

APPLE OR CRAB TREE, hand-colored engraving by David Martin. David Martin, *The British Flora*, 1794. (HA).

Hooker) after originals by Elizabeth Matthews and Frances Knight. Frances Knight, later Frances Acton, was the daughter of the author.

*T*URNING TO WORKS which have a predominantly artistic, rather than scientific emphasis, in their illustrations, the Cleveland collections include *A Select Collection of One Hundred Plates* (1775). It is the third issue of the work that was originally published from 1769 to 1770 featuring the plates of John Edwards, a British still-life and flower painter. Jacob George Strutt, the English painter and etcher who specialized in portraits and forest scenes, is represented by his *Sylva Britanica* (1822 to 1826). Trees and shrubs also are the subject matter of the plates engraved by William Clark from his own designs in Richard Morris's *Flora Conspicua* (1825 to 1826). Margaret Lace Roscoe is represented by the engravings with aquatint after her originals by Robert Havell, Jr., that appeared in her *Floral Illustrations of the Seasons* published from 1829 through 1831.

Perhaps the most celebrated of the ornamental flower books is *The Temple of Flora*

system. The work was issued in small sections apparently starting in 1798, although the earliest plate in either of the two Cleveland copies is 1799. A collective title page was issued in 1807 and bound volumes began being sold by Thornton subsequent to that date, all of which appear to vary in both the number of plates and the specific plates included. The Cleveland copies contain plates dating as late as 1812. The first two sections were illustrated by a series of engravings which constitutes the third part of Robert John Thornton's *New Illustration of the Sexual System of Carolus von Linnaeus* which was published from 1798 to 1810, although it bears a title page date of 1807. Thornton was a British physician and medical and botanical writer. As a physician, Thornton was successful, although somewhat controversial. He served as a doctor at the Marylebone Dispensary, where he is said to have introduced the use of digitalis for treating scarlet fever. He later succeeded Sir James Edward Smith as lecturer in medical botany at the united hospitals of Guy and St. Thomas.

Thornton's passion, however, was the production of the *New Sexual System,* which he first announced in 1797. The work was to be divided into three parts: the first was Linnaeus's prize essay on the sex of plants written in 1759; the second was to contain an exposition of the sexual system; and the third was to be *The Temple of Flora* featuring "picturesque botanical plates" illustrative of the

ROSES, color engraving by Richard Earlom after Robert John Thornton. Robert John Thornton, *The Temple of Flora* section, *New Illustrations of the Sexual System of Carolus von Linnaeus,* [1798-]1807[-1810]. (HA).

GROUP OF ROSES, color engraving by R. Rosse after Robert John Thornton. Robert John Thornton, ***The Temple of Flora***, 1812. (GC). Note the changes to the building in the back and the eggs which have hatched in the quarto version.

Group of Roses.

composed of portraits of the foremost authors associated with botanical works, miscellaneous botanical plates, and other mixed plates dealing with such diverse items as the eruptions of volcanoes, Biblical subjects, and the preparation of tea. The third section was composed of a series of color plates in various mediums including mezzotint, aquatint, stipple, line engraving, and various combinations of these processes. The colored plates of plants are among the most dramatic of all floral illustrations and are valued primarily for their contrasts, textures, and picturesque backdrops, while it is generally conceded that they are botanically worthless in terms of scientific illustration. The color plates also vary from copy to copy with some plates totally

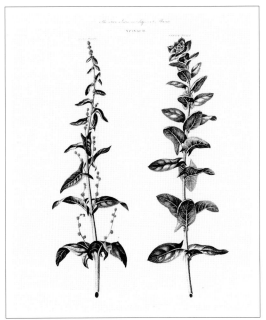

replaced by different plates and other plates reworked several times over the years producing multiple states. The copy at the Holden Arboretum appears to be earlier than the one owned by the Cleveland Medical Library Association since it has *The Queen* plate of 1804 illustrating the plant better known to us as the bird-of-paradise, *The Aloe* plate of 1798, and generally

THE TWO SEXES ON DIFFERENT PLANTS: SPINACH, one of the illustrative botanical plates from the first part of the work engraved by Caldwall after Henderson. Robert John Thornton, ***New Illustration of the Sexual System of Carolus von Linnaeus***, [1798-] 1807 [-1810]. (CMLA).

PORTRAIT OF WILLIAM WITHERING WITH VIGNETTE, engraving by William Ridley after Breda. Robert John Thornton, ***New Illustration of the Sexual System of Carolus von Linnaeus***, [1798-] 1807 [-1810]. (CMLA).

foremost painters practicing in England at the time, but with the exception of Sydenham Edwards and Peter Henderson, none of them are generally otherwise associated with botanical or floral illustration. The main artists in Thornton's stable included: Philip Reinagle who has been described by one writer as having been "noted chiefly for his pictures of dead game, hunting and sporting dogs, and shaggy ponies;" John Russell, portrait painter to the Queen; and Abraham Pether who was famous for his use of moonlight and firelight. Other plates were after earlier artists including Ehret, Aubriet, and John Miller, whose 1777 ***An Illustration of the Sexual System of Linnaeus*** was a forerunner of Thornton's work. Thornton himself supplied the original for the plate of roses accompanied by a pair of nightingales and their nest. Both the black prints and the colored prints were executed by the most notable etchers and engravers available including Francesco Bartolozzi, the popularizer of stipple engraving with whom Redouté studied on his trip to England; William Dunkarton who was celebrated for his work in mezzotint; and Joseph Stadler and Thomas Sutherland who were noted for their work in aquatint.

According to Nissen, the ***New Illustration*** also forms the fourth volume of Thornton's ***Botanical Extracts, or, Philosophy of Botany*** published in 1810, which Nissen cites as ***The Philosophy of Botany***. This work also features a large number of uncolored plates in the third volume with the greatest number of illustrations after originals by Peter Henderson, Warner, Sydenham Edwards, and Philip Reinagle, engraved mainly by Warner, Thomas Sutherland, and Peter Mazel. The Cleveland copy includes the plates of the eruptions of Mt. Vesuvius and of Mt. Etna and the plates of the picking and cooking of tea often found in copies of the ***New Illustration***.

early to middle stages of the other plates in the ***Temple of Flora***. The Cleveland Medical Library Association copy, on the other hand, has the *Queen Flower* plate of 1812, *American Aloe* plate of 1807, and generally middle to late states of the color plates, but it also has a much larger number of the uncolored plates for the first two parts than is present in the Arboretum copy.

The artists employed to provide the originals for the illustrations included some of the

Because of the expenses incurred in producing the ***New Illustration*** and particularly The

Temple of Flora, Thornton found himself in financial straits and was forced to petition Parliament in 1811 to allow him to conduct a lottery to try and recoup his losses. The grand prize was the collection of paintings for the *New Illustration*. The next level of prizes featured copies of *The Temple of Flora*, below those were copies of the plates for *The Temple of Flora*, the next round featured copies of the quarto version of *The Temple of Flora*, while below those were copies of the *British Flora*, and the bottom prizes were copies of *The Elements of Botany*. The Cleveland collections include the *British Flora*, which we have already mentioned, and a copy of the quarto version of *The Temple of Flora* at the Cleveland Botanical Garden.

The quarto version of *The Temple of Flora* was published from 1811 to 1812, apparently in the hope that a cheaper version of the work would lead to a boom in sales among the many who could not afford the folio edition. The plates are roughly copied from those in the folio edition, but they are generally regarded as more garish in color and differ in many details from the original plates. The main artists in this version are Philip Reinagle and Peter Henderson with the engravings mainly by R. Rosse, J. P. Quilley, Joseph Stadler, and W. M. Maddocks.

Peter Charles Henderson who provided botanical illustrations for most of Thornton's works was best known, prior to his botanical work for Thornton, for his genre studies, portraits, and miniatures. He is also represented in Cleveland by what appears to be a late issue of his *The Seasons* and *Treatise or General Instructions for Drawing and Painting Flowers*. The latter bears a publication date of 1806, plate

COLOR ENGRAVING by Peter Charles Henderson. Peter Charles Henderson, *The Seasons*, 1806 [-1807] [watermarks to 1816]. (GC).

dates of 1806 and 1807, but in this copy is printed on paper water-marked 1812 and 1816. The former portion of the work is mainly a florilegium arranged according to the seasons of the year, while the latter section provides basic instruction in floral painting.

This is one of several works on floral illustration in the collections. Another is Henrietta Maria Moriarty's *Viridarium* (1806). It features hand-colored stipple engravings of greenhouse plants with Linnaean names and rules of culture, but it was intended to foster the use of correct drawing in boarding schools.

HAND-COLORED ENGRAVING by Henrietta Maria Moriarty. Henrietta Maria Moriarty, *Viridarium*, 1806. (GC).

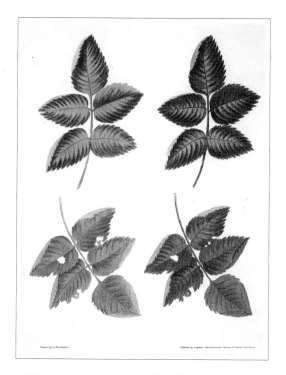

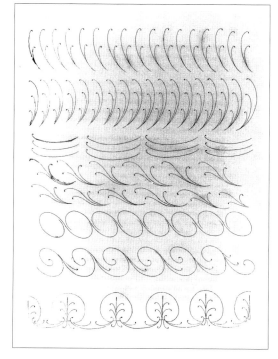

EXERCISE PLATE. George Brookshaw, *A New Treatise on Flower Painting*, 1818. (GC).

BRUSHSTROKE EXERCISE PLATE. George Brookshaw, *A New Treatise on Flower Painting*, 1818. (GC).

George Brookshaw, an artist best remembered for his pomological illustrations, was the author of *A New Treatise on Flower Painting* published in 1818. The work features hand-colored floral plates, a plate of practice brush strokes, color swatches to be matched, and uncolored plates for the aspiring student to practice painting. The *New Treatise* is basically concerned with the art of coloring rather than with any principles of design or botanical illustration.

A NEW ERA OF ILLUS-tration opened with the invention of lithography by Aloysius Senefelder in 1796. Based on the works in the Cleveland collections, the process does not appear to have played a major role in floral or botanical illustration until the 1820's. The earliest work that is definitely il-lustrated with lithographs in the collection is a made-up volume of plates after original illustrations by Valentine Bartholomew, who was flower painter to Queen Victoria and to the Duchess of Kent. The lithography is the work of Bartholomew's father-in-law, Charles Hullmandel, who popularized this form of illustration in England and would later invent the lithotint. The plates appear to be from Bartholomew's undated *Groups of Flowers* and from his *A Selection of Flowers* published from 1821 to 1822.

Hullmandel also did the color lithography for James Forbes' *Salictum Woburnense* of 1829 based upon the original art of James Stretford.

Other examples of British lithography of the period include the original plates by George and W. Spratt for George Spratt's *Flora Medica* published from 1827 to 1830 and the anonymous *Ten Lithographic Coloured Flowers with Botanical Descriptions* (there are actually 40 lithographed leaves of text and 40 lithographed plates in this work. The lithographer was R. H.

DALIA.

V. Bartholomew del.

Printed by C. Hullmandel.

London. Published by Rodwell & Martin New Bond St. Oct. 1.1821.

DALIA, color
lithograph by
Charles Hullmandel
after Valentine
Bartholomew.
Probably from
Valentine
Bartholomew,
*A Selection of
Flowers*, 1821-
1822. (HA).

Nimmo and the book was printed in Edinburgh in 1826.

To return to the continent, we find that the plates without text of José Mariano Conceiçao Velloso's *Florae Fluminensis Icones* (published at Paris from 1827 to 1832) feature lithographs by F. J. Knecht, who worked out of Senefelder's office in Paris, based on the original artwork of Velloso and Francisco Solano. The text by Velloso, who was a Franciscan clergyman and is regarded as the father of Brazilian botany, was published in 1825 in Rio de Janeiro and is not currently in the Cleveland collections.

The lithographic plates of Aimée Henry grace the *Plantae Officinales* of Theodor Friedrich Ludwig Nees von Esenbeck published in Dusseldorf from 1821 to 1833. The Holden Arboretum also has a related manuscript with watercolor paintings by C. F. and H. J. Martius entitled *Verzameling van officinale Planten Geteekend nar de Platen van Dr. Fr. L. Nees von Esenbeck*.

The Viennese school of art is represented in Daniel Wagner's *Pharmaceutisch-Medicinische Botanik* published at Vienna from 1828 to 1830. It features lithographs after drawings by Ignaz Strenzl. The state of the art in the low countries is represented by the *Sertum Botanicum* of the Société de Botanistes (1828 to 1832) with lithographic plates by Burggraaf which reproduce the artwork of G. Severeyns.

Turning to the North American continent, the Holden Arboretum has a bound volume of anonymous original watercolor paintings with the unpreposessing spine title of *Canadian Weeds*; fortunately, the contents bely the title and con-

PINK LADYSLIPPER, anonymous painting from the group bearing a binder's title of *Canadian Weeds*. (HA).

sist of a series of delicate illustrations of various wildflowers.

While there are not a great many illustrated works printed in America before our cut-off date in 1829, those that are present in the Cleveland collections are among the most important in the history of American illustration.

Two works, William P. C. Barton's *Vegetable Materia Medica of the United States,* published from 1817 to 1819, and Jacob Bigelow's *American Medical Botany,* published from 1817 to 1821, contend for the title of the first color printed botanical work (and by some accounts the first color printed book) to be produced in the United States.

Barton claims in his *A Flora of North America* issued from 1820 to 1824 (although bearing publication dates of 1821 to 1823) that some plates in the *Vegetable Materia Medica* represent the first color printing of illustrations in North America. He goes on to say that he is employing an imitation of the method used to illustrate Michaux (i.e., color stipple engraving) for some plates in *A Flora of North America* as well. The *Vegetable Materia Medica* featured engravings mainly by Tanner, Vallance, Kearny and Company, and with others by J. G. Warnicke and J. Boyd, all after Barton's originals; those in *A Flora* were engraved by Cornelius Tiebout (or Thiebout), F. Kearny, J. Boyd, C. Goodman, G. B. Ellis, I. L. Frederick, J. Drayton, and Jacob J. Plecher after Barton's originals, with those by Tiebout supposed to include the color stipplework. Although these claims may be true in some copies, since Gordon Dunthorne cites *A Flora* as the first American work to use the

French technique of color stipple engraving, it is not true of any of the copies of either work in the Cleveland collections—all of which have the stipplework printed in black and the colors painted over them.

Based upon the copies in the Cleveland collection, the claim of Barton's rival in American illustrated medical botanies is somewhat more credible, although a controversy exists over the media in which they were executed. Jacob Bigelow's *American Medical Botany* was originally begun with line engravings which were to be colored by hand. After the first 200 copies of the first ten plates were produced using this procedure, Bigelow decided that, given the amount of time this process took and the fact that an edition of 1000 copies was intended, he had to find a faster method of producing the color illustrations. The solution was to have the plates re-engraved using aquatint as the ground from which the color was to be printed. The plates were engraved by William B. Annin and George Girdler Smith after Bigelow's original artwork. Although Bigelow's writings would seem to suggest that the work featured conventional aquatint on copper plates, Richard J. Wolfe[7] has argued persuasively that the images were actually etched on stones with four imprints of the same image produced by each stone, the sheets cut, and a false platemark applied later. Whichever was the actual process used, the plates are clearly printed in color, and the Cleveland collections are fortunate enough to include copies with both the color printed and hand-colored versions of the first ten plates, as well as copies in the original wrappers.

Sir James Edward Smith's *A Grammar of Botany Illustrative of Artificial as well as Natural Classification* published in New York in 1822 is, according to Wolfe, the first work printed in the United States to have been illustrated by purely lithographic plates. The pictures are after the drawings of a Mr. Stansbury with the lithography executed by the litho-graphic press of Barnet and Doolittle in New York.

A somewhat later example of American lithography is found in Thomas Nuttal's *An Introduction to Systematic and Physiological Botany* published in Cambridge, Massachusetts, in 1827, which features lithography by Pendleton after the original artwork of Whitfield.

The Cleveland collections also possess two groups of nature prints. The earliest set was made by Jacques Necker de Saussure in 1801 and includes a ten leaf manuscript letter and a manuscript catalogue of the 308 species included in the 267 leaves of nature prints of Alpine plants. The set was privately produced as part of Necker's research, and he intended to offer it to a Dr. Gilibert in Paris.

The other set is a more commercial venture prepared by Marcellin Bonnet which bears the title *Facies Plantarum* on a printed title page published at Bordeaux in 1818. The Cleveland copy features 140 nature prints, a significant increase over the 45 plates which were published by Bonnet under the same title in 1810.

PRIMULA, A. INTEGRIFOLIA, B. AURICULA, nature prints by Jacques Necker de Saussure from his manuscript *Plantae Alpinae*, 1807. (HA).

---

[7] Richard J. Wolfe is a rare book librarian and historian. References are to his: Jacob Bigelow's American Medical Botany. North Hills, PA.: Bird & Bull Press; Boston, MA: Boston Medical Library, 1979.

Gardening and Landscape Architecture

HE CLEVELAND COLLECTIONS CONTAIN A wide variety of books relating to gardening and landscape architecture with the bulk of the strength located at the Cleveland Botanical Garden. Although considerations of space preclude a conclusive and detailed discussion of the works on gardening, we can examine a representative sampling of the material in the hope that it will give an idea of the range available in the collections.

Although not a primary collecting area, there are a number of agricultural works at the three libraries. Ancient agriculture is represented in the 1533 edition of ***Libri de Re Rustica***, which collects the agricultural writings of Cato, Varro, Columella, and Palladius. The ancients are also discussed in English in Richard Bradley's ***A Survey of the Ancient Husbandry and Gardening*** of 1725. An Italian poetic verse approach to the subject is taken in Luigi Alamanni's ***La Coltivazione*** (first published in 1546), which is represented in the collections by an edition of 1718. This work also includes Giovanni

Rucellai's ***Le Api***. Later, more practical works include items such as Frederick Butler's ***The Farmers Manual*** (1819) and William and Solomon Drowne's ***Compendium of Agriculture*** (1824).

While there are not many plant and seed catalogues in the collections, those that are present include some of the more innovative ones that were ever published. The ***Catalogus Plantarum*** composed by Philip Miller for the Society of Gardeners in England and published in 1730 features color mezzotint or mock-mezzotint illustrations. Although only one volume of the projected three volume work was actually published, it is important as an attempt by the English nurserymen and gardeners to establish a common nomenclature for garden plants that were being sold under a multitude of varying names.

In the chapter dealing with illustration, we have already mentioned such decorative catalogues as the numerous editions of Sweert's ***Florilegium*** and Robert Furber's ***Twelve Months of Flowers*** and ***Twelve Months of Fruits***. The

JUNE, handcolored engraving by Henry Fletcher after Peter Casteel. Robert Furber,
Twelve Months of Fruits, 1732. (HA).

collections also contain a sampling of more mundane garden catalogues from both Great Britain and the United States, chiefly from the nineteenth century. The majority of these are either in the collection of the Cleveland Botanical Garden or at the Cleveland Medical Library Association's Allen Library. Those at the Allen, including Michael Floy's *A Catalogue of Ornamental Trees, Flowering Shrubs, Herbaceous Plants, Bulbous Roots, and Fruit Trees* (1823), are of particular interest to Clevelanders and Ohioans since they were assembled and used in the area by Jared Potter Kirtland. Thus they reflect the local state of horticulture in the nineteenth century.

The books on general gardening begin with Charles Estienne's *De Re Hortensi Libellus*, a Latin tract aimed at children, which is present in the Paris and Lyons editions of 1539. Peter Lauremberg's *Horticultura, Libros II* (1631) and *Apparatus Plantarius* (1632), usually found bound together, were a major influence on Eu-

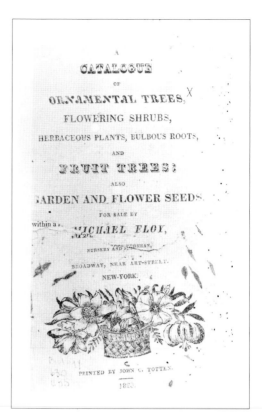

TITLE PAGE. Michael Floy, *A Catalogue of Ornamental Trees, Flowering Shrubs, Herbaceous Plants, Bulbous Roots, and Fruit*, 1823. Kirtland Collection (CMLA).

ropean gardening. Books by English authors include Thomas Hill's *The Arte of Gardening* published in 1608, Sir John Hill and Thomas Hale's *Eden* of [1756-]1757, Philip Miller's *The Gardeners Dictionary* of [1756-]1759, John Abercrombie and Thomas Mawe's *Everyman His Own Gardener* of 1784, and John Loudon's *An Encyclopaedia of Gardening* of 1824. The French authors are represented by the works of Nicolas de Bonnefons, Jean de La Quintinie, François Gentil, and Louis Liger.

Bonnefons, who was valet de chambre to the King of France, is represented by the 1672 edition of *The French Gardiner*. Jean de La Quintinie, the chief director of all gardens of the French King Louis, is represented by *The Complete Gard'ner* (1639), the first English edition of his work on orchids and herb gar-

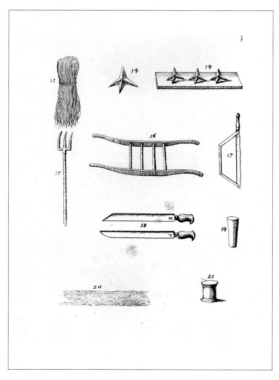

ENGRAVING OF GARDENING TOOLS.
Peter Lauremberg, *Horticultura, Libros II,* [1631]. (GC).

dens. Blanche Henrey[1] has suggested that LaQuintinie's work was translated by George Wise, with John Evelyn supervising or assisting, although Evelyn is known to have translated at least one part of the treatise. The translation is accompanied by Evelyn's *A Tract of the Making and Ordering of Wines in France*, and by *The English Vineyard Vindicated*. The latter is ascribed by the title page to John Rose, Keeper of the Royal Garden at St. James's Park, but is believed to have been actually written by Evelyn.

An anonymous French tract entitled the *Nouveau Traité de la Culture des Jardins Potagers*, dealing with kitchen gardens, is present in a Parisian edition of 1692.

Louis Liger, a noted French agriculturist, and François Gentil, a Carthusian lay brother who was the gardener to the Charter-house in Paris, are first represented in Cleveland by two English translations of their combined works, both of which appeared in 1706. Liger's *Le Jardinier Fleuriste et Historiographe* and Gentil's *Le Jardinier Solitaire* were translated anonymously into English. Their translation was revised by London and Wise, the noted gardeners and nurserymen, for an edition published as *The Retir'd Gardener.* A second anonymous translation of the works was published as *Le Jardinier Solitaire, the Solitary or Carthusian Gard'ner ... Also the Compleat Florist*. The Cleveland collections also include a 1716 German edition of the works and a 1708 French language edition of Liger's work.

Among the works dealing with American gardening are two editions published in London in 1821 of William Cobbett's *The American Gardener*. Cobbett is one of several politically controversial figures who worked in horticulture. Cobbett was a British subject who came to the United States by way of France to avoid imprisonment by the British government after publishing attacks on the financial speculations of his former superiors in the British army in Nova Scotia. His first stay in the

United States was spent initially teaching English to French refugees and translating material from French to English, but he soon got involved in American politics through the publication of pamphlets and several newspapers. Again Cobbett became the center of controversy, losing a $5,000 libel suit to Dr. Benjamin Rush of Philadelphia, whom he had ridiculed for excessively purging and bleeding yellow fever victims. This resulted in Cobbett's return to England, where he published a 36 volume parliamentary history of England before publishing an article attacking severe military flogging. The latter earned him a two year prison term and a thousand pound fine that led to his financial ruin. Following this catastrophe, he returned to the United States in 1817 in order to escape a second prison term for subsequent publications. He spent two years operating a seed store in New York and then returned to England, where he established a seedfarm in Kensington and drifted in and out of trouble as a result of his continuing political publications.

The collections also include a number of works cast in the form of gardener's calendars which provide instruction on gardening chores organized by the months of the year. These include a copy of the tenth edition of John Evelyn's *Kalendarium Hortense* published in 1706, the first edition of John Laurence's *The Fruit-Garden Kalendar* published in 1718, and the twelfth edition of Philip Miller's *The Gardeners Kalendar* published in 1760.

American examples include Bernard McMahon's *The American Gardener's Calendar* published in 1806, generally regarded as the first best selling gardening book to be written and published in the United States. Its author was an Irishman who had immigrated to the United States, where he worked for a time for a printer in Philadelphia before establishing his nurseries in 1802. He went on to become one of the most important nurserymen in the

[1]Blanche Henrey is a specialist in British publications on botany and horticulture through the 18th century. Reference is to her *British Botanical and Horticultural Literature before 1800.* 3 vol. London: Oxford University Press, 1975.

United States and was responsible for introducing many of the botanical discoveries of the Lewis and Clark Expedition to the gardens of the Eastern United States through his propagation of the plants from the seeds and roots from the expedition. These were made available to him through his friendship with Thomas Jefferson.

Grant Thorburn was another British citizen whose efforts at political reform, like those of Cobbett, landed him in jail and forced him to flee to the United States. After losing his initial means of making a living as a nailmaker because of the introduction of a nailmaking machine, Thorburn went into business as a seedsman. He supplemented his income by writ-

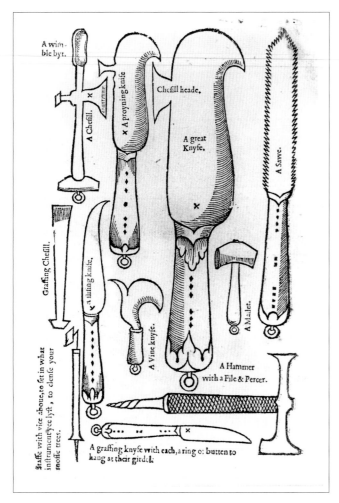

WOODCUTS OF PRUNING AND GRAFTING TOOLS. Davy Brossard, ***A Booke of the Arte and Maner, Howe to Plant and Graffe All Sortes of Trees,*** 1572. (GC).

ing fiction under the pen-name of Lawrie Todd. He is represented in the collections by the third edition of his ***The Gentleman and Gardener's Calendar*** (1821), which includes ads for seed and supplies sold by Thorburn.

Other books in the collections deal with specific subjects, plants, or groups of plants. In this area, we find the 1572 second edition of Leonard Mascall's English translation of Davy Brossard's book on grafting published as ***A Booke of the Arte and Maner, Howe to Plant and Graffe All Sortes of Trees***. Other later specialized texts include William Speechly's ***A Treatise on the Culture of the Pine Apple*** (1779), geared to hothouse cultivation in Northern England, James MacPhail's ***A Treatise on the Culture of the Cucumber*** (1794), Thomas Watkins's ***The Art of Promoting the Growth of the Cucumber and Melon*** (1824), William Forsyth's ***A Treatise on the Culture and Management of Fruit Trees*** (1802), William Coxe's ***A View of the Cultivation of Fruit Trees and the Management of Orchards and Cider*** (1817), and James Thacher's ***The American Orchardist*** (1822).

The collection also includes two *Hesperides*. Although named for the land where mythology had the daughters of Atlas tend and guard golden apples, the golden and other colored fruit referred to in these works belong to the citrus family. The earlier of the two is the first edition of Giovanni Baptista Ferrari's ***Hesperides*** published in 1646, one of the first works devoted entirely to citrus fruit. It dealt with citrus growing in Southern Italy and includes engravings of an orangerie and hot-house along with plates of the fruits themselves. The second work, Jan Commelin's ***Nederlantze Hesperides*** (1676), is even more intriguing since it deals with growing oranges in the northern climate of the Netherlands.

Another specialized area represented in the collections is that of viticulture and winemaking. We have already mentioned ***The English Vineyard Vindicated*** by John Rose and John Evelyn published in 1672. Other English works on the same subject represented in Cleveland include the anonymous *The Vineyard* published in 1732, with a dedication signed by "S. J.", and William Speechly's *A Treatise on the Culture of the Vine* published in 1790.

The United States is represented by the first edition of John Adlum's *A Memoir on the Cultivation of the Vine in America* (1823). Adlum, who was an American botanist, horticulturist, vintner, and nurseryman, maintained a farm and nursery in what is now the Georgetown section of Washington, D.C., where he experimented with both foreign and domestic grapes. He is perhaps best remembered for being responsible for the propagation of the Catawba grape, which he called *Tokay*.

Another American work on viticulture is *The American Vine-dresser's Guide* of John James Dufour published in 1826. The author was a Swiss viticulturist. After hearing complaints from French officers returning from the American Revolution about the scarcity of wine in America, he came to the United States with an eye toward entering the wine business. He operated vineyards in Kentucky and Indiana, and as this work demonstrates, got caught up in a silkworm propagation craze that was sweeping the United States at the time. He advocated growing the grapes around mulberry trees which would be used to raise silkworms. The Cleveland copy,[2] which is at the Allen Library, is of particular interest since it bears a signed inscription from the author to Jared Potter Kirtland.

Floristic works include the second edition of Charles de Monstereul's *Le Floriste François* published in 1658, the second edition of Isaac Emmerton's *A Plain and Practical Treatise on the Culture & Management of the Auricula, Polyanthus, Carnation, Pink, and the Ranunculus* published in 1819, and the second and third editions of Thomas Hogg's *A Concise and Practical Treatise on the Growth and Culture of the Carnation, Pink, Auricula, Polyanthus, Ranunculus, Tulip, Hyacinth, Rose, and Other Flowers* published

respectively in 1822 and 1824. The Cleveland Medical Library Association's George Gehring Marshall Collection of Herbals also contains an unpublished manuscript in the same vein. The manuscript is entitled *The Cultivation of Auriculas and Carnations*, although it also deals with tulips, anemones, and polyanthus. The author of the work was Samuel Brewer, who, after failing in the woolen business and losing 20,000 pounds and a family estate, became head-gardener to the Duke of Beaufort at Badminton. The treatise is accompanied by a letter from Brewer to the Reverend George Harbin, who served as chaplain and librarian to the Earl of Weymouth and also had charge of the gardens at Longleat.

*T*URNING FROM practical gardening to decorative gardening and landscape architecture, the practices of the Ancient Romans are demonstrated in a description of the villas of Pliny at Laurentia and Tuscany accompanied by diagrams in *Les Plans et les Descriptions des Plus Belles Maisons de Campagne de Pline le Consul* written by the French antiquarian, Jean François Felibien, and represented by the second edition of 1706. The work demonstrates the Roman adoption of the Greek concept of the garden court and the general garden as an extension of the living area of the house. Although the collections do not have any early works discussing the extension of this concept to terraces that became a feature in many Italian gardens, the terraces themselves may be viewed in engravings in works such as Giovanni Battista Falda's *Li Giardini di Roma* published circa 1680.

Designs for parterres, the raised beds arranged in intricate designs which were popular in Italian and French formal gardens, are the

FRONTISPIECE by J. Fletcher after R. Cooper. S. J., *The Vineyard*, 1732. (GC).

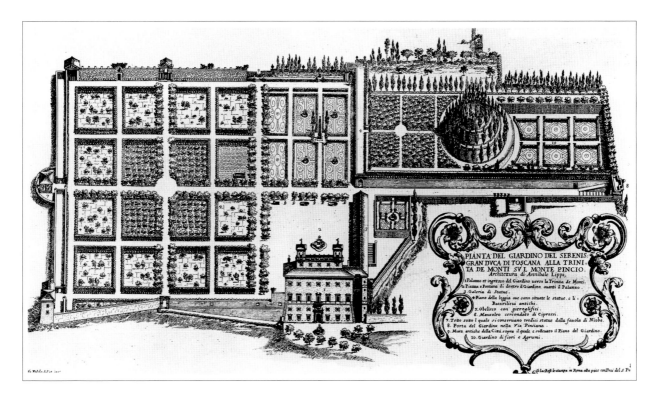

ENGRAVED PLAN OF THE GARDEN OF THE DUKE OF TUSCANY. Giovanni Battista Falda,
Li Giardini di Roma, circa 1680. (GC).

subject matter of Pierre Betin's *Le Fidelle Jardinier* published in 1636.

The elaborate formal gardens of France served as the inspiration for Antonie Joseph Dezallier D'Argenville's *La Theorie et la Pratique du Jardinage* first present in the anonymous first edition of 1709. The author, who held several important positions in the French court, is most famous for his *Abrégé de la Vie des Plus Fameux Peintres* (1745-1752). He is cryptically identified in the third French edition of 1713, which is also in Cleveland, by the initials "L. S. A. I. D. A." which have been identified as standing for La Sieur Antoine Joseph Dezallier d'Argenville. The work covers the range of French formal elements including parterres, the geometrical patterns of avenues, the use of bodies of water and fountains, and even the hydraulics involved in them.

Later French works include P. J. Galimard's *Architecture de Jardins* (circa 1765), Gabriel Thouin's *Plans Raisonés de Toutes les Espèces de Jardins* (1820), the third edition of Pierre

Boitard's *Traité de la Composition et de l'Ornement des Jardins* (1825), and Richou's *Art de Composer, de Distribuer et de Décorer, a Peu de Frais, Toute Espèce de Jardin* (1828-1829).

The handiworks of the French formal gardeners are amply portrayed in a number of illustrated works. These include an undated *Versailles Illustrated* published by John Bowles circa 1740 that includes illustrations of the charming fountains based on *Aesop's Fables*, J. Mérigot, Jr.'s, *Promenades ou Itineraire des Jardins de Chantilly* published in 1791, Count Alexandre L. J. Laborde's *Description des Nouveaux Jardins de la France et de ses Anciens Chateaux* published from 1808 through 1815, and the anonymous souvenir booklet, *Vues et Descriptions du Jardin des Plantes* published in 1813.

Turning to England, the collections include Batty Langley's *New Principles of Gardening,* which began publication in 1727 but bears an imprint of 1728. Langley was an architect, gardener, landscape designer, and surveyor. This latter training makes itself clear in the first part

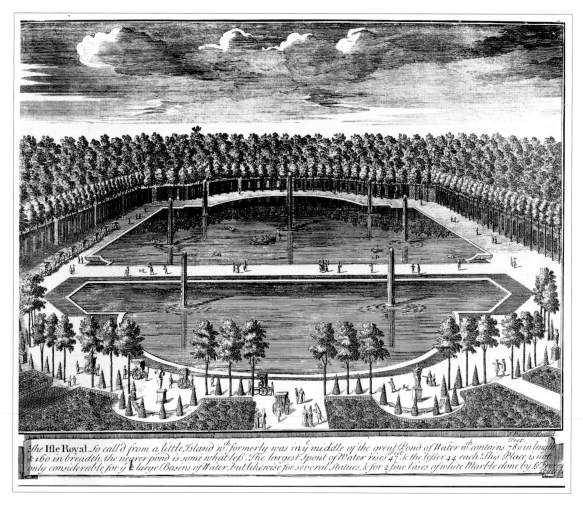

The Isle Royal. So call'd from a little Island wch formerly was in y.^e middle of the great Pond of Water w. contains 780 in length & 160 in breadth, the nearer pond is some what less. The largest Spout of Water rises 47^{Feet}. & the lesser 44 each. This Place is not only considerable for ye large Basins of Water, but likewise for several Statues, & for 2 fine Vases of white Marble done by L^e P...

THE ISLE ROYAL, engraving by John Bowles. John Bowles, *Versailles Illustrated*, circa 1740. (GC).

of his book which deals with geometry for garden design and would suggest that Langley favored the formal patterns of the great French landscapers. After discussing the needs of kitchen, fruit, flower, market, nursery, and physic gardens, Langley turns his attention to a brief discussion of garden design in general. Langley's suggestions, which take the form of a series of points (some of which seem contradictory), contain many of the elements which are associated with the English school of landscape gardening represented by William Kent, Capability Brown, and Humphry Repton. Although following the French classical school in his concern for lines of sight developed to their extremity and ending in focal points such as woods, ruins, buildings, etc., he at the same time argues against the artifices of parterres and

topiaries and advocates a broad elegant lawn in front of houses. Beyond the lawn and the house, however, he appears to favor irregular woods with labyrinths and winding paths that suddenly open to reveal a surprising flower bed or statue.

These latter features look forward to the theories of landscape architecture espoused by Sir William Chambers in his *A Dissertation on Oriental Gardening,* which is represented in the Cleveland collections by the third edition of 1773. Chambers is reputed to have been of Scottish ancestry, although he was born in Sweden and served in his youth as a supercargo with the Swedish East India Company, journeying to Bengal and China. He later studied architecture in Paris and Italy before setting up practice as an architect in England, where his works

‹120›

included Somerset House and the pagoda at Kew Gardens. Although he served at various times as architectural tutor to the Prince of Wales, Comptroller of the King's Works, and Surveyor-General, and was one of the founders of the Royal Society, his knighthood was in the Swedish Order of the Polar Star, a title he was allowed to use in England in much the same manner as in the case of Sir John Hill.

Like Hill, Chambers was a contentious figure. In one stroke, his work attacked the formal geometric gardens of the French school with their rooms formed of hedge walls, displays of topiaries, and their overly regular fountains with cascades going down marble steps, and the English school of William Kent and Capability Brown with their emphasis on large green lawns, serpentine paths, with an occasional temple, or cluster of trees, and a shrub boundary on one side. Chambers argued that the French designs were too artificial while the English were too simple. He suggested that the gardens of the Chinese provide the inspiration for a middle ground.

Despite the celebrity of the *Dissertation*, it is not as clear what Chambers is actually proposing as what he is opposed to. He explains on the one hand that the aim of the Chinese is to imitate the beauties of Nature, goes to some length to point out that the primary consideration in garden design is that established by the natural topography of the land, and emphasizes that the landscaping for buildings should reflect the purpose and architecture of the buildings. Yet, what he ultimately seems to be advocating is something resembling Batty Langley's twisting path through wooded copses, with each turn of the path revealing a new small scene of a statue, a pretty flower garden, a tomb or ruin, with other scenes designed to be more effective at different times of the day or seasons of the year. Thus the landscape as a whole would be full of both variety and of material for intellectual stimulation.

In the course of the *Dissertation*, Chambers described a number of Chinese gardens in detail, emphasizing the introduction of elements to stimulate the viewer with aspects that were either pleasing, terrifying, or surprising in their nature. This aspect in particular inspired William Mason and Horace Walpole to write a poetic satire on Chambers's work entitled *An Heroic Epistle in Answer to Sir William Chambers, Knight.* This proved more popular than the original work by Chambers as evidenced by the fact that the third edition of the *Dissertation* is accompanied by the eleventh edition of the *Heroic Epistle*. Although the *Heroic Epistle* is cast in the form of a parody of Chambers's work, the subject of the satire has much more to do with English politics and society than with any defense of the English school of landscape gardening.

Imbedded in the third edition of William Marshall's *On Planting and Rural Ornament,* published in 1803, is the text of Horace Walpole's *Essay on Modern Gardening,* which was originally written in 1770 and first published in 1780.

The largest concentration of works on landscape architecture in the collections are those by Humphry Repton, the successor to Capability Brown as the leading exponent of the English school of architecture. Repton came from a mercantile family and began his career as a general merchant. Unfortunately, Repton's mercantile enterprises were less than successful, and after losing money in John Palmer's mail-coach enterprise, he decided to become a landscape gardener.

When Repton was employed to remodel an estate, he visited the estate to take notes which would then be formulated into a plan. Repton would write his recommendations and accompany them with painted maps of the estate and views of various parts of it, the latter illustrated as they originally appeared and as they would appear after his improvements were installed. These before and after pictures were accomplished by the use of overlays, which Repton termed *slides*, that portrayed the original scene on the overlays and the scene as improved by Repton on the painting underneath. The manuscript and illustrations were gathered and bound in leather to form what Repton termed a *Red Book*, which was then presented to the property owner.

The Holden Arboretum has one of these *Red Books* prepared in 1793 and 1794 for Charles Tibbets's estate of Barton Seagrave in Northamptonshire. Repton's suggestions in this instant were relatively modest. His main recommendations were the removal of some of the trees that were planted in rows in the old style so as to give a more natural appearance to the landscape, changing the route of the road so that it was not so near the house (and thus competing with it in the landscape), and opening the stream bed so that it would give a broader expanse of water.

The *Red Books* served as the sources for Repton's published works, with portions of his discussions usually transferred verbatim to the printed form and the illustrations reproduced in what have been termed some of the finest aquatints of the period. The earliest of these publications is an oblong folio, undated but known to have been published in 1794, that bore the title of *Sketches and Hints on Landscape Gardening*. Repton explained that he chose this title with some care since he could not formulate absolute rules because each landscape must be considered individually with reference to the topography involved and the style of house which was present. One of the more interesting of Repton's theories, which is first formulated in this work, is his suggestion that it is beneficial to introduce cattle into landscapes both to break down banks and give a natural appearance to ponds and streams and to give perspective to the landscape.

To move from the particular to the more general, Repton is generally viewed as carrying on and developing the English tradition of Capability Brown. Like Brown, Repton places a heavy emphasis on an improved natural setting, with the main features comprised of a large expanse of open grass, generally unbroken sightlines, irregular groupings of trees, and a serpentine path. Repton, however, was more concerned with integrating the physical building into the landscape. In this regard, he sometimes suggested major alterations in the architecture of the buildings, but he is more noted for his reintroduction of terraces and his use of flower gardens to provide a transitional point between the house and the great lawn.

BARTON SEAGRAVE, painting by Humphry Repton. Humphry Repton's manuscript, ***Barton Seagrave in Northamptonshire, a Seat of Charles Tibbets***, 1793-1794. (HA).

His other books in the Cleveland collections include *Observations on the Theory and Practice of Landscape Gardening* (1803), *An Enquiry into the Changes of Taste in Landscape Gardening* (1806), and *Fragments on the Theory and Practice of Landscape Architecture* (1816). Also in the collections are both an 1808 edition and an undated later edition of Repton's *Designs for the Pavillon at Brighton.* They were never implemented because of problems with funding and were superceded by the designs of John Nash.

An essential part of the English school of landscape gardening was the display of large trees either singly or in groupings. The importance of trees in both the English economy and landscape was brought home by John Evelyn in 1674 in response to complaints by the Commissioners of the Navy to the Royal Society about the lack of trees for shipbuilding. Their short supply was due to their consumption for domestic fuel, their abuse by the iron and glass industries that deforested large areas for charcoal and then simply moved on to raze another region when the trees ran out, and the increasing conversion of forest land to fields and pastureland. Evelyn brought together his own ideas and those of others in the Society in the publication of *Sylva. Sylva* aroused the passions of the country and led to a prolonged period of tree-planting for both aesthetic and economic considerations. Unfortunately, much of the timber planted in response to Evelyn's book was consumed by the British Navy in its series of wars with the French. This led to the plea for a new round of reforestation by the Scottish physician, Alexander Hunter, in his edition of Evelyn's *Silva* (the spelling having been changed). It was first published in 1776 and is first represented in the Cleveland collections by the 1786 edition. It was with the knowledge that Hunter's edition was in preparation that the Edinburgh nurseryman, William Boutcher, prepared his *A Treatise on Forest-trees*, with in-

structions for improving plantations, which was first published in 1775.

The need for trees for shipbuilding was felt in France as well, where it manifested itself in the mission of the Michauxs to America and in the writings of Duhamel du Monceau and his successors, which we have already referred to in previous chapters. The continental view of the English school of landscaping is represented in the collections by Ercola Silva (Count of Biardrate), *Dell'Arte dei Giardini Inglesi* (circa 1800); while the English reverence for trees is brought home in works such as Jacob George Strutt's *Sylva Britannica* of 1822 to 1826, with its illustrations of notable specimens.

The next generation after Repton's is represented by John Claudius Loudon in his *A Treatise on Forming, Improving, and Managing Country Residences* (1806). In this early work, Loudon took great pains to attack numerous aspects of Repton's work, including Repton's inconsistency (on which point he apparently missed Repton's central thesis that each project must be treated differently since each depends upon a different topography and different style of architecture in its buildings). He also attacked Repton for his use of reflecting lakes to replace running streams, his destruction of a natural dell to put in a road, and his destruction of "ancient trees" (ignoring the point that the trees removed were usually planted in ungainly rows). Yet, despite Loudon's protestations and his substitution of the term *picturesque improvement* for *landscape gardening*, one cannot help but feel that his emphasis on returning to a more natural order emulates the same claim made by Repton in his attack on the successors of Capability Brown. Perhaps we are really seeing a continuation of the evolution of the English style of gardening and landscape architecture rather than a radical departure from it.

Index and Bibliography
Primary Sources

The following is a list of the books and artwork cited as primary texts in the Cleveland collections. Books followed by the symbol CMLA are at the Allen Memorial Medical Library of the Cleveland Medical Library Association. Those followed by GC are in the Eleanor Squire Library of the Cleveland Botanical Garden, and those followed by HA are in the Warren H. Corning Library of the Holden Arboretum. The bold numbers immediately following the location symbols are the entry numbers for those items in Stanley H. Johnston, Jr.'s *The Cleveland Herbal, Botanical, and Horticultural Collections: A Descriptive Bibliography of Pre-1830 Works from the Libraries of the Holden Arboretum, the Cleveland Medical Library Association, and the Garden Center of Greater Cleveland* (Kent, Ohio, and London: Kent State University Press, 1992), and are for those who would like more detailed accounts of individual items. The reader is also referred to the bibliography in that work for the list of secondary sources used in compiling the present volume. This list also serves as an index to the present volume with the numbers in plain roman type indicating page references for text and italics indicating page references for illustrations.

Abercrombie, John, and Thomas Mawe. *Everyman His Own Gardener*. London: 1784. GC. **553**.114.

Acosta, Cristobal. *Aromatum & Medicamentorum in Orientali India Nascentium Liber*. Antwerp: 1593. HA. **137**. 15.

—. *Tractados de las Drogas, y Medicinas des las Indias Orientales*. Burgos: 1578. HA. **117**. 15.

Adanson, Michel. *Familles des Plantes*. Paris, 1763. HA. **461**. 45.

Adlum, John. *A Memoir on the Cultivation of the Vine in America*. Washington, DC: 1823. CMLA. **865**. 118.

Alamanni, Luigi. *La Coltivazione*. Padua: 1718. GC. **339**. 112.

Alpini, Prospero. *De Medicina Aegyptorum*. Paris: 1645. CMLA. **205**. 15.

—. *De Plantis Aegypti Liber* and *Liber de Balsamo*. Venice: 1592. HA. **136**. 34.

—. *De Plantis Exoticis Libri Duo*. Ed. by A. Alpini. Venice: 1627. HA. **175**. 34.

Amatus Lusitanus. *In Dioscoridis Anazarbei De Medica Materia Libros Quinque Enarrationes*. Lyons: 1558. CMLA. **79**. 10.

Andrews, Henry C. *The Botanists Repository*. London: 1797-1814. GC, HA. **641**. 100.

—. *Coloured Engravings of Heaths*. London: [1793-]1802-1809. HA. **674**. 100, *100*.

—. *Roses*. London: 1805-1828. HA. **699A**. 100, *100*.

Anguillara, Luigi. *Semplici*. Venice: 1561. HA. **84**. 11.

Apuleius Barbarus. *Herbarium*. [Rome: 1483]. HA. **5**. 1, 57, *1*.

Artedi, Petrus. *Ichthyologia*. Ed. by C. Linnaeus. Leyden: 1738. HA. **43**.

Aubriet, Claude. Original painting. HA. **MS3**. 71, *71*

Balmis, Francisco Xavier de. *Demostracion de las Eficaces Virtudes Nuevamente Descubiertas en las Raices de Dos Plantas de Nueva-España, Especies de Ágave y de Begónia*. Madrid: 1794. HA. **621**. 14.

Bartholomaeus Anglicus. *De Proprietatibus Rerum*. Strassburg: 1485. CMLA. **8**. 33.

Bartholomew, Valentine. *Groups of Flowers* (plates from). London. HA. **849**. 108.

—. *A Selection of Flowers* (plates from). London: 1821-1822. HA. **849**. 108, *109*.

Barton, Benjamin Smith. *Collections for an Essay towards a Materia Medica of the United States*. Philadelphia, PA: 1810. CMLA, HA. **739**. 27.

Barton, John. *A Lecture on the Geography of Plants*. London: 1827. HA. **917**. 56.

Barton, William Paul Crillon. *A Flora of North America*. Philadelphia, PA: [1820-]1821-1823[-1824]. CMLA, HA. **850**. 110.

—. *Vegetable Materia Medica of the United States*. Philadelphia, PA: 1817-1819. CMLA. **803**. 28, 110, *28*.

Bauer, Francis. *Delineations of Exotick Plants Cultivated at Kew*. London: [1793-]1796-1803. HA. **638**. 82, *83*.

Bauhin, Gaspard. *Pinax, Theatri Botanici*. Basel: 1623. CMLA. **171**. 38.

Baylis, Edward. *A New and Compleat Body of Practical Botanic Physic*. London: 1791. HA. **609**. 23.

Belon, Pierre. *De Arboribus Coniferis*. Paris: 1553. CMLA. **73**. 34.

—. *Les Observations de Plusieurs Singularitez et Choses Memorables Trouvees en Grece, Asie, Judée, Egypte, Arabie & Autres Pays Estranges*. Paris: 1553. CMLA. **131**. 34.

Bergeret, Jean Pierre. *Phytonomatotechnie Universelle*. Paris: 1783[-1786]. HA. **550**. 45.

Berkenhout, John. *Clavis Anglica Linguae Botanicae*. London: 1764. HA. **467**. 48.

Besler, Basilius. *Hortus Eystettensis*. Nuremberg: 1613. CMLA. **159**. 65, 66.

Bessa, Pancrace. Original paintings. HA. **MS17**. 90.

Betin, Pierre. *Le Fidelle Jardinier*. Paris: 1636. HA. **192**. 119.

Bigelow, Jacob. *American Medical Botany*. Boston, MA: 1817-1820[-1821]. CMLA, HA. **804**. 28, 110-111, *28*.

—. *Florula Bostoniensis*. Boston, MA: 1814. CMLA, GC, HA. **771**. 51.

—. *Florula Bostoniensis*. Boston, MA: 1824. CMLA. **873**. 51.

Blackwell, Elizabeth. *A Curious Herbal*. London: 1737-1739. CMLA, HA. **386**. 23, *23*.

—. *Herbarium Blackwellianum*. Nuremberg: 1757-1765. CMLA. **444**. 24, *24*.

Bock, Hieronymus. *De Stirpium Commentariorum Libri Tres* (with Benoît Textor's *De Stirpium Differentiis Libellus*). Trans. by D. Cyber. Strassburg: 1552. HA. **71**. 6, 59, *59*.

—. *Kreuter Buch*. Strassburg: 1546. CMLA. **66**. 6, *59*.

—. *New Kreütter Buch*. Strassburg: 1539. HA. **52**. 6, 59, *6*.

Boitard, Pierre. *Traité de la Composition et de l'Ornament des Jardins*. Paris: 1825. GC. **892**. 119.

Bondt, Jakob de. *De Medicina Indorum*. Paris: 1645. CMLA. **205**. 15.

Bonelli, Giorgio, and Niccolo Martelli. *Hortus Romanus*. Rome: 1772-1793. HA. **509**. 47, 76, *46*.

Bonnefons, Nicolas de. *The French Gardiner*. Trans. by J. Evelyn. London: 1672. CMLA. **245**. 114.

Bonnet, Charles. *Recherches sur l'Usage des Feuilles dans les Plantes*. Gottingen and Leyden: 1754.
HA. **435**. 41.

Bonnet, Marcellin. *Facies Plantarum*. Bordeaux: 1818. HA. **808**. 111.

Bonpland, Aimé. *Description des Plantes Rares Cultivées a Malmaison et a Navarre*. Paris: [1811-]1813
[-1817]. HA. **770**. 88.

Boslarn, Joseph von. Original paintings with manuscript text. HA. **MS2**. 73, *75*.

Boutcher, William. *A Treatise on Forest-trees*. Edinburgh: 1775. HA. **521**. 123.

Boym, Michael. *Flora Sinensis*. Vienna: 1656. HA. **220**. 16, *17*.

Bradley, Richard. *A Survey of the Ancient Husbandry and Gardening*. London: 1725. GC. **352**. 112.

Brewer, Samuel. *The Cultivation of Auriculas and Carnations*. (manuscript) ca. 1710. CMLA. **MS4**. 117.

Bright, Timothy. *A Treatise wherein Is Declared the Sufficiencie of English Medicines ... and A Collection of
Medicines Growing ... within Our English Climat*. London: 1615. CMLA. **161**. 21.

Brookshaw, George. *A New Treatise on Flower Painting*. London: 1818. GC. **809**. 108, *108*.

Brossard, Davy. *A Booke of the Arte and Maner, Howe to Plant and Graffe All Sortes of Trees*. Trans. by
L. Mascall. London: 1572. GC. **107**. 116, *116*.

Brotero, Felix Avellar de. *Compendio de Botanica*. Paris: 1788. HA. **580**. 49.

—. *Phytographia Lusitania Selectior*. Lisbon: 1816-1827. HA. **792**. 49.

Brunfels, Otto. *Contrafayt Kreüterbüch*. Strassburg: 1532. CMLA. **43**. 4, 58, *58*.

—. *Herbarum Vivae Eicones*, *Novi Herbarii Tomo II*, and *Tomus Herbarii III*. Strassburg: 1532;
1531-1532; 1536. CMLA. **42**. 4, 10, 57-58, *5*.

—. *In Dioscoridis Historiam Herbarum Certissima Adaptio*. Strassburg: 1543. HA. **60**. 9, 58, *58*.

Brunschwig, Hieronymus. *A Most Excellent and Perfecte Homish Apothecarye*. Cologne: 1561. CMLA,
HA. **85**. 22.

Bry, Johann Theodor de. *Anthologia Magna*. Frankfurt: 1626. CMLA. **174**. 63, *63*.

—. *Florilegium Novum*. Oppenheim: 1612[-1614]. CMLA. **158**. 63.

Buc'hoz, Pierre Joseph. *Collection Coloriée des Plus Belles Variétées de Jacinthes*. Paris: 1781. GC,
HA. **540**. 69.

—. *Collection Coloriée des Plus Belles Variétées de Tulipes*. Paris: 1781. GC, HA. **541**. 69.

—. *Collection Precieuse et Enluminée des Fleurs*. Paris: 1776-1779. HA. **528**. 69, *70*.

—. *Histoire Universelle du Règne Végétal*. Paris: [1774-]1775-1780. HA. **524**. 68-69.

—. *Le Jardin d'Eden*. Paris: [1781-]1783[-1784]. HA. **548**. 69.

Burmann, Nicolas Laurens. *Flora Indica* and *Prodromus Florae Capensis*. Leyden: 1768. HA. **486**. 47.

Burwell, Lewis. *Observations on the Digitalis Purpurea*. Philadelphia, PA: 1805. CMLA. **694**. 14.

Butler, Frederick. *The Farmer's Manual*. Hartford, CT: 1819. CMLA. **820**. 112.

Byam, Lydia. A *Collection of Fruits from the West Indies*. London: 1800. HA. **656**. 102, *103*.

Canadian Weeds. HA. **MS16**. 110, *110*.

Candolle, Augustin Pyramus de. *Icones Plantarum Galliae Rariorum*. Paris: 1808. HA. **723**. 91.

—. *Plantarum Succulentarum Historia*. Paris: 1799[-1805]. GC, HA. **651**. 86, *86*.

—. *Plantes Rares du Jardin de Genève*. Geneva: 1825-1829. GC, HA. **903**. 92.

Canvane, Peter. *A Dissertation on the Oleum Palmae Christi*. Bath: London: [1764?]. GC. **475**. 14, *14*.

Catesby, Mark. *Hortus Britanno-Americanus*. London: 1763. HA. **462**. 49, 78.

—. *The Natural History of Carolina, Florida, and the Bahama Islands*. Rev. by G. Edwards.
London: 1771. HA. **501**. 49.

Cavanilles, Antonio José. *Icones et Descriptiones Plantarum, Quae aut sponte in Hispania Crescunt.* Madrid: 1791-1801. HA. **610**. 49.

——. *Monadelphiae Classis Dissertationes Decem.* Paris and Madrid: 1785-1790. HA. **563**. 49.

Cesalpino, Andrea. *De Plantis Libri XVI.* Florence: 1583. HA. **122**. 33.

Chambers, William. *A Dissertation on Oriental Gardening.* Dublin: 1773. GC. **510**. 120-121.

Chaumeton, François Pierre, Jean Chamberet, and Pierre Jean François Turpin. *Flore Médicale.* Paris: 1814-1820. HA. **782**. 91.

——. *Flore Médicale* (manuscript). Paris: 1814. HA. **MS23**. 91, *91*.

Cobbett, William. *The American Gardener.* London: 1821. CMLA. **841**. 115.

——. *The American Gardener.* Stereotype edition. London: 1821. GC. **842**. 115.

Coles, William. *Adam in Eden.* London: 1657. CMLA. **222**. 21, 22.

Colla, Tecophile. *Plantes Plus Rares Fleuries dans le Jardin de Monsieur l'Avocat Colla Peinte d'après Nature.* (manuscript). 1819. HA. **MS24**. 96, *97*.

Collaert, Adrian. *Florilegium.* Antwerp: ca. 1590. HA. **132**. 62, *63*.

College of Physicians of London. *Pharmacopoeia Londinensis.* Trans. by N. Culpeper. London: 1653. CMLA. **213**. 22.

——. *Pharmacopoeia Londinensis.* Trans. by N. Culpeper. London: 1669. CMLA. **242**. 22.

——. *Pharmacopoeia Londinensis.* Trans. by W. Salmon. London: 1691. CMLA. **291**. 22.

Commelin, Jan. *Nederlantze Hesperides.* Amsterdam: 1676. HA. **257**. 116.

Commelin, Jan, and Caspar Commelin. *Horti Medici Amstelodamensis.* Amsterdam: 1697; 1701. GC, HA. **304**. 15, *16*.

Contant, Jacques, and Paul Contant. *Les Oeuvres.* Poitiers: 1628. HA. **177**. 11, *11*.

Cordus, Valerius. *Annotationes in Dioscoridem, Historiae Stirpium Libri IV, De ArtificiososExtractionibus Liber, Compositiones Medicinales,* and *Liber Quintus* (with Benedictus Aretius' *Stocc-Hornii et Nessi in Bernantium ... Montium, & Nascentium in Eis Stirpio Descriptio,* and Conrad Gesner's *De Hortis Germaniae*). Ed. by C. Gesner. Strassburg: 1561. CMLA. **86**. 7.

——. *Dispensatorium.* Leyden: 1608. CMLA. **152**. 7.

——. *Stirpium Descriptionis Liber Quintus.* Strassburg: 1563. CMLA. **86**. 7.

Cornut, Jacques. *Canadensium Plantarum Historia.* Paris: 1635. GC. **190**. 49.

Coxe, John Redman. *The American Dispensatory.* Philadelphia, PA: 1806. CMLA. **702**. 27.

Coxe, William. *A View of the Cultivation of Fruit Trees and the Management of Orchards and Cider.* Philadelphia, PA: 1817. CMLA, GC. **796**. 116.

Culpeper, Nicholas. *The English Physician Enlarged.* London: 1662. CMLA. **232**. 22.

Curtis, William. *Botanical Magazine.* London: 1787-present. GC (first 57 volumes), HA (fullrun). **577**. 98, *98*.

——. *Flora Londinensis.* London: [1775-]1777-1798. CMLA (111 plates only), GC, HA. **532**. 98-99.

——. *Lectures on Botany.* London: 1803-1804. HA. **686**. 99.

Dalechamps, Jacques. *Historia Generalis Plantarum.* Ed. by J. Bauhin and J. Desmoulins. Lyons: 1587; 1586. HA. **129**. 36.

Dalibard, Thomas François. *Florae Parisiensis Prodromus.* Paris: 1749. GC. **421**. 44.

Darwin, Erasmus. *The Botanic Garden.* London: 1791. GC. **604**. 48.

——. *Phytologia.* London: 1800. CMLA. **657**. 49.

Descourtilz, Michel Etienne. *Flore Pittoresque et Médicale des Antilles*. Paris: [1821-]1827-1833. HA. **926**. 92.

Desfontaines, Réné Louiche. *Flora Atlantica*. Paris: 1798[-1799]. HA. **645**. 86.

Dezallier D'Argenville, Antonie Joseph. *La Theorie et la Pratique du Jardinage*. Paris: 1709. GC. **324**. 119.

——. *La Theorie et la Pratique du Jardinage*. Paris: 1713. HA. **329**. 119.

Digby, Kenelm. *Of Bodies and of Mans Soul ... with Two Discourses of the Powder of Sympathy, and of the Vegetation of Plants*. London: 1669. CMLA. **243**. 36.

Dioscorides, Pedanios. *De Materia Medica Libri Quinque*. Ed. by C. Sprengel. Leipzig: 1829-1830. CMLA. **968**. 9.

——. *De Materia Medica Libri Sex*. With emendations by P. A. Mattioli. Lyons: 1554. CMLA. **74**. 9.

——. *De Medica Materia Libri VI*. Trans. by J. Ruel. Lyons: 1543. CMLA. **61**. 9.

——. *De Medicinali Libri Sex*. Trans. by J. Ruel. Lyons: 1552. CMLA. **72**. 9.

——. *De Medicinali Materia*. Trans. by E. Barbaro, ed. by G. B. Egnazios. Venice: 1516. CMLA. **28**. 9.

——. *Della Materia Medicinale*. Trans. by M. Montesiano. Firenze: 1546-1547. CMLA. **69**. 9.

——. *Kreutter Buch*. Trans. by J. Dantzius. Frankfurt: 1546. CMLA. **67**. 9.

——. *Les Six Livres de la Matiere Medicinale*. Trans. by M. Matthée. Lyons: 1559. HA. **81**. 9.

Dodoens, Rembert. *Florum et Nonnullarum Herbarum Historia*. Antwerp: 1568. CMLA, HA. **97**. 34, 61.

——. *Florum et Nonnullarum Herbarum Historia*. Antwerp: 1569. CMLA. **100**. 34.

——. *Frumentorum, Leguminum, et Herbarum Historia*. Antwerp: 1566. CMLA, HA. **95**. 34, 61.

——. *Histoire des Plantes*. Trans. and ed. by C. L'Ecluse. Antwerp: 1557. CMLA. **78**. 19, 34-35.

——. *Historia Frumentorum, Leguminum, Palustrium et Aquatilium Herbarum*. Antwerp: 1569. CMLA. **101**. 35.

——. *A Niewe Herball*. Trans. by H. Lyte. London: 1578. CMLA. **118**. 19.

——. *Stirpium Historiae Pemptades Sex*. Antwerp: 1583. CMLA. **123**. 19, 34.

Drapiez, Pierre Auguste Joseph. *Herbier de l'Amateur de Fleurs*. Brussels: 1828-1835. HA. **941**. 90.

Drowne, William and Solomon. *Compendium of Agriculture*. Providence, RI: 1824. GC. **875**. 112.

Duchesne, Antoine-Nicolas. *Manuel de Botanique*. Paris: 1764. HA. **468**. 44.

Du Choul, Jean. *De Varia Quercus Historia, Accessit Pylati Montis Descriptio*. Lyons: 1555. HA. **75**. 34.

Dufour, John James. *The American Vine-dresser's Guide*. Cincinnati, OH: 1826. CMLA. **908**. 117.

Duhamel du Monceau, Henri Louis. *La Physique des Arbres*. Paris: 1758. HA. **445**. 42.

——. *Traité des Arbres et Arbustes*. Paris: 1755. HA. **439**. 60, 87, 87.

——. *Traité des Arbres et Arbustes*. Paris: [1800-]1804-1819. HA. **662**. 87, 87.

Duppa, Richard. *The Classes and Orders of the Linnaean System of Botany*. London: 1816. CMLA. **786**. 49.

Durante, Castore. *Herbario Novo*. Venice: 1602. HA. **150**. 61, 61.

Eaton, Amos. *Botanical Exercises*. Albany, NY: 1820. CMLA. **830**. 55.

——. *A Manual of Botany for the Northern and Middle States*. Albany, NY: 1818. CMLA. **811**. 55.

——. *A Manual of Botany for the Northern and Middle States of America*. Albany, NY: 1824. CMLA. **876**. 55.

——. *A Manual of Botany for the Northern States*. Albany, NY, 1817. CMLA. **797**. 54.

Eaton, Amos, William E. A. Aikin, and Hezekiah H. Eaton. *A Manual of Botany for North America*. Albany, NY: 1829. CMLA. **954**. 55.

Edwards, John. *A Select Collection of One Hundred Plates*. London: 1775. HA. **222**. 103.

Edwards, Sydenham Teast. *The Botanical Register*. London: 1815-1847. HA. **784**. 99, 101, *99*.

Ehret, Georg Dionysius. Original paintings. GC (1), HA (6). **MS10**. 79, *79*.

Emmerton, Isaac. *A Plain and Practical Treatise on the Culture & Management of the Auricula, Polyanthus, Carnation, Pink, and the Ranunculus*. London: 1819. GC. **822**. 117.

Estienne, Charles. *De Re Hortensi Libellus*. Paris: 1539. CMLA. **53**. 114.

——. *De Re Hortensi Libellus*. Lyons: 1539. CMLA. **54**. 114.

——. *De Latinis et Graecis Nominibus Arborum, Fruticum, Herbarum, Piscium & Avium Liber*. Paris: 1544. CMLA. **63**. 33, 114.

Evelyn, John. *Kalendarium Hortense*. London: 1706. CMLA, GC. **318**. 115.

——. *Silva* and *Terra*. York and London: 1786. HA, GC. **567**. 80, 123.

——. *Silva* and *Terra*. York and London: 1812. CMLA. **759**.

——. *A Tract of the Making and Ordering of Wines in France*. See Bonnefons, Nicolas de. *The French Gardiner*.

Falda, Giovanni. *Li Giardini di Roma*. Rome: 1680. GC, HA. **270**. 117, *119*.

Felibien, Jean François. *Les Plans et les Descriptions des Plus Belles Maisons de Campagne de Pline le Consul*. Amsterdam: 1706. GC. **319**. 117.

Ferrari, Giovanni Baptista. *De Florum Cultura Libri IV*. Rome: 1633. CMLA, GC, HA. **184**. 63.

——. *Hesperides*. Rome: 1646. HA. **206**. 116.

Feuillée, Louis. *Journal des Observations Physiques, Mathematiques et Botaniques Faites par l'Ordre du Roy sur les Côtes Orientales de l'Amerique Meridionale, & dans les Indes Occidentales, depuis l'Année 1707, jusques en 1712*. Paris: 1714; 1725. HA. **334**. 42.

Fleming, John. *A Catalogue of Indian Medicinal Plants and Drugs*. Calcutta: 1810. CMLA. **740**. 16.

Florilegium (manuscript). Nuremberg: eighteenth century. CMLA. **MS13**. 73, *74*.

Floy, Michael. *A Catalogue of Ornamental Trees, Flowering Shrubs, Herbaceous Plants, Bulbous Roots, and Fruit Trees*. New York, NY: 1823. CMLA. **866**. 114, *114*.

Forbes, James. *Salictum Woburnense*. London: 1829. HA. **956**. 108.

Forster, Johann Reinhold. *Flora Americae Septentrionalis*. London: 1771. HA. **502**. 49.

Forsyth, William. *A Treatise on the Culture and Management of Fruit Trees*. Philadelphia, PA: 1802. GC. **672**. 116.

Fuchs, Leonhart. *De Historia Stirpium Commentarii Insignes*. Basel: 1542. CMLA, HA. **59**. 7, 58-59, *7*.

——. *L'Histoire des Plantes Reduicte en Tres Bon Ordre*. Lyons: 1575. HA. **112**. 59.

——. *New Kreüterbuch*. Basel: 1543. CMLA, GC. **62**. 7, 58.

——. Proofs before letters of illustrations for the *New Kreüterbuch*, proofs of woodcuts for its unpublished continuation, and reprints from the blocks for the *De Historia Stirpium*. HA. **62 notes**. 58, *59*.

Furber, Robert. *The Flower-Garden Display'd*. London: 1734. GC. **377**. 65.

——. *Twelve Months of Flowers*. London: 1730. HA. **367**. 65, 112.

——. [*Twelve Months of Fruits*]. London: 1732. HA. **375**. 112, *113*.

Galimard, P. J. *Architecture de Jardins*. Paris: ca. 1765. HA. **479**. 119.

Genlis, Stéphanie Félicité Ducrest, Countess of. *Emblemes et Devises* (manuscript). 1821. HA. **MS25**. 92, *95*.

Gerard, John. *The Herball*. London: 1597[-1598]. CMLA, HA. **143**. 19-20, 62.

——. *The Herball*. Enl. and rev. by T. Johnson. London: 1633. CMLA, GC, HA. **185**. 20, *20*.

Gerard, Louis. *Flora Gallo-provincialis*. Paris: 1761. CMLA. **454**. 44.

Gesner, Conrad. *Opera Botanica*. Ed. by C. C. Schmiedel. Nuremberg: 1751-1771. CMLA. **432**. 60.

Gleichen-Russworm, Wilhelm Friedrich. *Decouvertes les Plus Nouvelles dans le Regne Vegetal*. Trans. by
    J. F. Isenflamm. Nuremberg: 1770. GC. **497**. 38, *39*.

Goethe, Johann Wolfgang von. *Versuch die Metamorphose der Pflanzen zu erklären*. Gotha: 1790.
    GC. **596**. 56.

Le Grant Herbier. Paris: [c. 1499]. CMLA. **23**. 3, *3*.

Green, Thomas. *The Universal Herbal*. Liverpool: [1816-1820]. CMLA. **793**. 26.

The Grete Herball. London: 1526. CMLA. **36**. 3, 18, *18*.

Grew, Nehemiah. *The Anatomy of Plants*. London: 1682. CMLA, HA. **274**. 37.

Gronovius, Joannes Fredericus. *Flora Virginica*. Leyden: 1762. GC, HA. **456**. 49.

Hales, Stephen. *Statica de Vegetabili ed Analisi dell'Aria*. Trans. by D. M. A. Ardinghelli. Naples: 1776.
    CMLA. **525**. 41.

    —. *Statical Essays*. London: 1727-1733. CMLA. **362**. 41, *41*.

    —. *Vegetable Staticks*. London: 1727. CMLA. **362**. 41.

Haller, Albrecht von. *Historia Stirpium Indigenarum*. Helvetiae. Berne: 1768. HA. **488**. 47.

Henderson, Peter. *The Seasons* and *A Treatise, or General Instructions for Drawing and Painting Flowers*.
    London: 1806-1807[-1816]. GC. **711**. 107, *107*.

Herbarius Latinus (with German synonyms). Mainz: 1484. CMLA, HA. **6**. 2, 57, *2*.

Herbarius Latinus (with German synonyms). Passau: 1485. CMLA. **9**. 2.

Herbarius Latinus (with German synonyms). Passau: 1486-1487]. HA. **12**. 2.

Herbarius Latinus. Vicenza: 1491. GC. **15**. 2, *57*.

Herbarius Latinus. Venice: 1499. CMLA. **21**. 2.

Herbarius Latinus. Venice: 1509. CMLA. **25**. 2.

Herbier Colorié (manuscript). Italy: eighteenth century. HA. **MS12**. 73, *74*.

Herbolario Volgare. Venice: 1536. CMLA. **48**. 2.

Heyland, Jean Christoph. Original paintings. c. 1840. HA. 95, *95*.

Hill, John. *The British Herbal*. London: 1756[-1758]. CMLA, GC, HA. **441**. 23.

    —. *The Family Herbal*. Bungay: 1812. CMLA, GC. **760**. 23, 99.

    —. *A General Natural History*. London: 1748-1752. CMLA. **420**. 23.

    —. *A History of the Materia Medica*. London: 1751. CMLA. **A3**. 23.

Hill, John, and Thomas Hale. *Eden*. London: [1756-]1757. GC, HA. **442**. 114.

Hill, Thomas. *The Arte of Gardening*. London: 1608. HA. **153**. 114.

Hogg, Thomas. *A Concise and Practical Treatise on the Growth and Culture of the Carnation, Pink, Auricula,*
    Polyanthus, Ranunculus, Tulip, Hyacinth, Rose, and Other Flowers. London: 1822. GC. **858**. 117.

    —. *A Concise and Practical Treatise on the Growth and Culture of the Carnation, Pink, Auricula,*
    Polyanthus, Ranunculus, Tulip, Hyacinth, Rose, and Other Flowers. London: 1824. GC. **878**. 117.

Hooke, Robert. *Micrographia*. London: 1665. CMLA. **237**. 36, *37*.

Hooker, William Jackson. *Exotic Flora*. London: [1822-]1823-1827. CMLA, GC, HA. **869**. 102.

Hortus Sanitatis. Mainz: 1491. CMLA. **16**. 2, 57, *4*.

Hortus Sanitatis. Strassburg: 1497. HA. **20**. 57.

Hughes, Griffith. *The Natural History of Barbados*. London: 1750. HA. **425**. 78.

Hughes, William. *The American Physitian*. London: 1672. CMLA. **246**. 16.

Humboldt, Friedrich Heinrich Alexander von. *De Distributione Geographica Plantarum Secundum Coeli Temperiem et Altitudinem Montium, Prolegomena*. Paris: 1817. HA. **798**. 56.

Humboldt, Friedrich Heinrich Alexander von, and Aimé Bonpland. *Monographie des Melastomacées*. Paris: [1806-]1816. HA. **794**. 56, 91, *91*.

——. *Plantes Equinoxiales*. Paris: [1805-]1808-1809[-1817]. HA. **729**. 56, 91.

Hutten, Ulrich von. *De Guaiaci Medicina et Morbo Gallico*. Mainz: 1519. CMLA. **31**. 14.

Ibn Butlan. *Tacuini Sanitatis*. Strassburg: 1531. CMLA. **41**. 58.

J., S. *The Vineyard*. London: 1732. GC. **376**. 117, *118*.

Jacquin, Nicolaus. *Florae Austriacae ... Icones*. Vienna: 1773-1778. HA. **512**. 82.

——. *Hortus Botanicus Vindobonensis*. Vienna; 1770-1776. HA. **500**. 82.

——. *Icones Plantarum Rariorum*. Vienna, London, Leyden, and Strassburg: 1781-1793[-1795]. HA. **545**. 82.

——. *Observationum Botanicarum Iconibus ab Auctore Delineatis Illustratarum*. Vienna: 1764-1771. HA. **474**. 82.

——. *Selectarum Stirpium Americanarum Historia*. Vienna: 1763. HA. **463**. 80.

——. *Selectarum Stirpium Americanarum Historia*. Vienna: c. 1780. HA. **539**. 80, 82, *80, 81*.

Jaume Saint-Hilaire, Jean Henri. *La Flore et la Pomone Françaises*. Paris: 1828[-1835]. HA. **662**. 92.

——. *Plantes de la France*. Paris: [1805-]1808[-1809]. HA. **730**. 92, *91*.

Josselyn, John. *New-Englands Rarities Discovered*. London: 1672. CMLA. **247**. 16, *17*.

Jussieu, Antoine-Laurent de. *Genera Plantarum Secundum Ordines Naturales Disposita*. Paris: 1789. HA. **591**. 45.

Kaempfer, Engelbert. *Amoenitatum Exoticarum Politico-physico-medicarum Fasciculi V*. Lemgo: 1712. HA. **327**. 42.

Knorr, Georg Wolfgang. *Thesaurus Rei Herbariae Hortensisque Universalis*. Nuremberg: 1750 [1771-1772]. HA. **427**. 79.

Knight, Thomas Andrew. *Pomona Herefordiensis*. London: 1811 [1820]. GC. **756**. 102, *103*.

Kops, Jan. *Flora Batava*. Amsterdam: [1800-]1807-1836. CMLA, HA. **663**. 97, *97*

Laborde, Alexandre L. J. *Description des Nouveaux Jardins de la France et de ses Anciens Chateaux*. Paris: 1808[-1815]. HA. **731**. 119.

La Brosse, Guy de. *De la Nature, Vertu, et Utilité des Plantes*. Paris: 1628. HA. **178**. 36.

Lambert, Aylmer Bourke. *A Description of the Genus Pinus*. London: 1828[-1829]. HA. **944**. 82.

Langley, Batty. *New Principles of Gardening*. London: 1728 [1727]. HA. **363**. 119.

La Quintinie, Jean de. *The Compleat Gard'ner*. Trans. by J. Evelyn or G. London. London: 1693. HA. **293**. 114.

Laurence, John. *The Fruit-garden Kalendar*. London: 1718. GC. **340**. 115.

Lauremberg, Peter. *Horticultura, Libros II*. Frankfurt: 1631. CMLA, GC. **181**. 114, *114*.

——. *Apparatus Plantarius*. Frankfurt: 1632. CMLA, GC. **183**. 114, *114*.

L'Ecluse, Charles. *Exoticarum Libri Decem*. [Leyden]: 1605. CMLA, HA. **151**. 36.

——. *Rariorum aliquot Stirpium per Pannonium et Austriam Observatarum Historia*. Antwerp: 1583[-1584]. GC, HA. **126**. 35, 61.

——. *Rariorum aliquot Stirpium per Hispanias Observatarum Historia*. Antwerp: 1576. HA. **113**. 35, 61.

——. *Rariorum Plantarum Historia*. Antwerp: 1601. CMLA, HA. **149**. 36.

——. *Stirpium Nomenclator Pannonicus*. Antwerp: 1584. GC, HA. **127**. 36.

Ledermüller, Martin Frobenius. *Mikroscopische Gemüths und Augen Ergötzung*. Nuremberg: 1760-1783. CMLA. **453**. 38.

—. *Versuch, bëy angehender Frühlings Zeit die Vergröszerungs Werckzeuge* ... Nuremberg: 1764. GC, HA. **471**. 38.

Leeuwenhoek, Antony van. *Epistolae Physiologicae Super Compluribus Naturae Arcanis*. Delft: 1719. CMLA. **342**. 38.

—. *Ontledingen en ontdekkingen van het Begin der Planten in de Zaden van Boomen*. Leyden: 1685. CMLA. **279**. 37.

—. *Ontledingen en ontdekkingen van de Cinnaber Naturalis*. Leyden: 1686. CMLA. **282**. 38.

—. *The Select Works*. Trans. by S. Hoole. London: 1798-1799. HA. **646**. 38.

—. *Vervolg der Brieven*. Leyden: 1688. CMLA. **286**. 38.

Leoniceno, Niccolo. *De Plinii & Pluriam Aliorum Medicina Erroribus*. Ferrara: 1509. CMLA. **26**. 33.

L'Héritier de Brutelle, Charles Louis. *Cornus*. Paris: 1788 [1798]. HA. **586**. 86.

—. *Geraniologia*. Paris: 1787-1788 [1791]. HA. **578**. 86.

—. *Hymenopappus*. c. 1788. HA. **585**. 84.

—. *Sertum Anglicum*. Paris: 1788 [1789-1792]. HA. **587**. 85, 95.

—. *Stirpes Novae*. Paris: 1784-1785[-1791]. HA. **555**. 84, *84*.

—. Unpublished plates. HA. **555 notes**. 84, *85*.

Libri de Re Rustica. Venice: 1533. CMLA. **44**. 112.

Liger, Louis. *Le Jardinier Fleuriste et Historiographe*. Amsterdam: 1708. CMLA. **323**. 115.

Liger, Louis, and François Gentil. *Le Jardinier Fleuriste et Historiographe* (in German). Leipzig: 1716. CMLA. **337**. 115.

—. *Le Jardinier Solitaire, the Solitary or Carthusian Gard'ner ... also the Compleat Florist*. London: 1706. CMLA. **321**. 115.

—. *The Retir'd Gard'ner*. Trans. by London and Wise. London: 1706. CMLA. **320**. 115.

Lincoln, Almira Hart. *Familiar Lectures on Botany*. Several places: 1829. HA. **959**. 55.

Lindern, Franz Balthasar. *Tournefortius Alsaticus*. Strassburg: 1728. HA. **364**. 40.

Lindley, John. *Digitalium Monographia*. London: 1821. GC. **844**. 82.

—. *Rosarum Monographia*. London: 1820. HA. **832**. 102.

Linnaeus, Carl. *Amoenitates Academicae*. Various places: 1749-1790. HA. **424**. 44.

—. *Bibliotheca Botanica*. Halle: 1747. HA. **412**. 43.

—. *A Dissertation on the Sexes of Plants*. Trans. by J. E. Smith. London: 1786. HA. **568**. 48.

—. *The Families of Plants*. Trans. by a Botanical Society at Lichfield. Various places: 1787. CMLA, GC (vol. 1 only), HA. **572**. 48.

—. *Fauna Svecica*. Leyden: 1746. HA. 44.

—. *Flora Lapponica*. Amsterdam: 1737. HA. **385**. 43.

—. *Flora Zeylanica*. Stockholm: 1747. HA. **414**. 44.

—. *Fundamenta Botanica*. Paris: [1743-]1744. HA. **403**. 43.

—. *Genera Plantarum*. Paris: 1743. HA. **400**. 43.

—. *Genera Plantarum*. Stockholm: 1754. HA. **437**. 43.

—. *Genera Plantarum*. Stockholm: 1764. HA. **472**. 43.

—. *Genera Plantarum*. Ed. by J. C. D. Schreber. Frankfurt: 1789-1791. HA. **594**. 43.

—. *Hortus Cliffortianus*. Amsterdam: 1737. GC, HA. **387**. 42, 78, *43*.

—. *Hortus Upsaliensis*. Stockholm: 1748. HA. **416**. 44.

—. *An Introduction to Botany*. Trans. by J. Lee. London: 1794. CMLA. **623**. 48.

—. *Musa Cliffortiana*. Leyden: 1736. HA. **381**. 42.

—. *Museum Alpho-Fridericianum*. Stockholm: 1746. HA. 44.

—. *Museum Tessinianum*. Stockholm: 1753. HA. 44.

—. *Philosophia Botanica*. Tournai: 1824. HA. **879**. 43.

—. *Praelectiones in Ordines Naturales Plantarum*. Ed. by P. D. Giseke. Hamburg: 1792. HA. **614**. 44.

—. *A Selection of the Correspondence of Linnaeus and Other Naturalists*. Ed. by J. E. Smith. London: 1821. CMLA. **845**. 44.

—. *Species Plantarum*. Stockholm: 1753. GC. **434**. 43, *43*.

—. *Species Plantarum*. Stockholm: 1762-1763. HA. **458**. 43-44.

—. *A System of Vegetables*. Trans. by a Botanical Society at Lichfield. London: [1782-]1783 [-1784]. CMLA. **549**. 48.

—. *Systema Naturae*. Paris: 1744. HA. **403**. 44.

—. *Systema Naturae*. Stockholm: 1758-1759. HA. **446**. 44.

—. *Systema Naturae*. Stockholm: 1766-1768. CMLA, HA. **481**. 44.

Linnean Society of London. *Transactions*. London: 1791-1807. CMLA. **612**. 48.

L'Obel, Matthias de. *Icones Stirpium seu Plantarum tam Exoticarum, quam Indigenarum*. Antwerp: 1591. CMLA. **135**. 62.

—. *Plantarum seu Stirpium Historia*. Antwerp: 1576. CMLA. **114**. 19, 35.

Loddiges, Conrad, and Sons. *The Botanical Cabinet*. London: 1817-1833. HA. **806**. 101.

Loiseleur-Deslongchamps, Jean Louis Auguste. *Flore Gallica*. Paris: 1806-1807. HA. **712**. 92.

Loudon, John Claudius. *An Encyclopaedia of Gardening*. London: 1824. GC. **880**. 114.

—. *A Treatise on Forming, Improving, and Managing Country Residences*. London: 1806, GC. **704**. 123.

Lovell, Robert. *Pambotanologia*. Oxford: 1665. CMLA. **238**. 21.

Macer Floridus. *De Herbarum Virtutibus* (with Walahfrid Strabo's *Hortulus*). Freiburg: 1530. CMLA. **40**. 3.

—. *De Viribus Herbarum*. [Paris?: ca. 1515]. CMLA. **27**. 3.

McMahon, Bernard. *The American Gardener's Calendar*. Philadelphia, PA: 1806. CMLA, HA. **705**. 115.

MacPhail, James. *A Treatise on the Culture of the Cucumber*. London: 1794. GC. **624**. 116.

Malo, Charles. *Histoire des Tulipes*. Paris: ca. 1821. CMLA. **853**. 90.

Malpighi, Marcello. *Opera omnia*. London: 1686. CMLA. **283**. 37.

Manardo, Giovanni. *Epistolae Medicinales*. Paris: 1528. CMLA. **38**. 10.

—. *Epistolarum Medicinalium Libri Duodeviginti*. Basel: 1525. CMLA. **46**. 10.

Marshall, Humphry. *Arbustrum Americanum*. Philadelphia, PA: 1785. CMLA, HA. **558**. 50.

Marshall, William. *On Planting and Rural Ornament*. London: 1803. GC. **681**. 121.

Martin, David. *The British Flora*. Sheffield: [1794]. HA. **625**. 102, *102*.

Martius, C. F., and H. J. Martius. *Verzameling van Officinale Planten Geteekend nar de Platen van Dr. Fr. L. Nees von Esenbeck* (manuscript). HA. 110.

Martyn, John. *Historia Plantarum Rariorum*. London: 1728[-1737]. HA. **365**. 77, *77*.

Martyn, Thomas. *Twenty-four Additional Letters*. London: 1794. CMLA. **627**. 53.

Mason, William, and Horace Walpole. *An Heroic Epistle in Answer to Sir William Chambers, Knight*. See Chambers, William. *A Dissertation on Oriental Gardening*.

Mattioli, Pier Andrea. *Commentarii in Libros Sex Pedacii Dioscoridis Anazarbei De Materia Medica* and *Apologia Adversus Amathum Lusitanum*. Venice: 1558. CMLA. **80**. 10.

—. *Commentarii in Sex Libros Pedacii Dioscoridis Anazarbei De Medica Materia*. Venice: 1565. HA. **93**. 10, 60.

—. *Commentarii in VI. Libros Pedacii Dioscoridis Anazarbei De Materia Medica*. Venice: 1583. GC. **124**. *10*.

—. *De Plantis Epitome*. Ed. by J. Camerarius. Frankfurt: 1586. CMLA, HA. **128**. 10, 60, *61*.

—. *I Discorsi ne i Sei Libri della Materia Medicinale di Pedacio Dioscoride Anazarbeo*. Venice: 1555. CMLA. **77**. 10, 60.

—. *New Kreüterbuch*. Translated by G. Handsch. Prague: 1563. CMLA. **89**. 10, 60.

Maund, Benjamin. *The Botanical Garden*. London: 1825-1826[-1851]. CMLA, GC, HA. **905**. 101.

—. *The Botanic Garden*. Royal edition. London: ca. 1830. HA. **905**. 101, *101*.

Medical Botany. London: 1819-1821. CMLA. **854**. 25.

Meerburgh, Nicolaas. *Plantae Rariores Vivis Coloribus Depictae*. Leyden: 1789. HA. **592**. 97, *97*.

—. *Plantarum Selectarum Icones Pictae*. Leyden: 1798. HA. **643**. 97.

Merian, Maria Sibylla. *Histoire des Insectes de l'Europe*. Amsterdam: 1730. HA. **368**. 65, *64*.

—. *Receuil de Plantes des Indes*. Paris: ca. 1745. HA. **407**. 65.

Merian, Matthaeus. *Florilegium Renovatum*. Frankfurt: 1641. HA. **203**. 63.

Mérigot, J. *Promenades ou Itinéraire des Jardins de Chantilly*. Paris: 1791. HA. **606**. 119.

Michaux, André. *Histoire des Chênes de l'Amérique*. Paris: 1801. HA. **667**. 50, 87.

Michaux, François André. *Histoire des Arbres Forestiers de l'Amérique Septentrionale*. Paris: 1810-1813. HA. **747**. 50, 87.

—. *Histoire des Pins et des Sapins de l'Amérique Septentrionale*. Paris: 1810. HA. **741**. 50, 87.

—. *The North American Sylva*. Paris: 1819. HA. **824**. 50, 87.

—. *Voyage a l'Ouest des Monts Alléghanys dans les États de l'Ohio, du Kentucky et du Tennessée, et Retour a Charleston*. Paris: 1804. HA. **692**. 50.

Miles, Charles. *A New and Improved System of Medical Botanical Practice*. Cleveland, OH: 1829. CMLA. **962**. 31, *31*.

Miller, Philip. *Figures of the Most Beautiful, Useful, and Uncommon Plants Described in the Gardeners Dictionary*. London: 1771. HA. **503**. 80.

—. *The Gardeners Dictionary*. London: [1756-]1759. GC. **448**. 114.

—. *The Gardeners Kalendar*. London: 1760. CMLA. **450**. 115.

Milne, Colin. *A Botanical Dictionary*. London: 1805. GC. **696**. 99.

Monardes, Nicolas. *De Simplicibus Medicamentis Ex Occidentali India Delatis*. Abridged and trans. by C. L'Ecluse. Antwerp: 1574. CMLA. **110**. 15.

—. *Joyfull Newes out of the New-Found Worlde*. Trans. by J. Frampton. London: 1596. CMLA. **140**. 15.

—. *Simplicium Medicamentorum Ex Novo Orbe Delatorum*. Trans. and abridged by C. L'Ecluse. Antwerp: 1593. HA. **137**. 15.

Monroe, John. *The American Botanist, and Family Physician*. Comp. by S. Gaskill. Wheelock, VT: 1824. CMLA. **882**. 29.

Monstereul, Charles de. *Le Floriste François*. Rouen: 1658. CMLA. **224**. 117.

Morandi, Giambattista. *Historia Botanica Practica*. Milan: 1744. HA. **404**. 73.

Mordant de Launay, Jean Claude Michel, and Jean Louis Auguste Loiseleur-Deslongchamps. *Herbier Général de l'Amateur*. Paris: [1810-]1816-1827. HA. **795**. 90.

—. *Herbier Général de l'Amateur* (manuscript). HA. **MS22**. 90, *90*.

Moriarty, Henrietta. *Viridarium*. London: 1806. GC. **706**. 107, *107*.

Morison, Robert. *Plantarum Historiae Universalis Oxoniensis*. Oxford: 1680; 1699. HA. **269**. 40.

—. *Plantarum Umbelliferarum*. Oxford: 1672. HA. **248**. 38.

Morris, Richard. *Flora Conspicua*. London: [1825-]1826. HA. **915**. 103.

Muhlenburg, Henry. *Catalogus Plantarum Americae Septentrionalis*. Lancaster, PA: 1813. CMLA. **766**. 51.

—. *Descriptio Uberior Graminum et Plantarum Calamariarum Americae Septentrionalis Indigenarum et Cicurum*. Philadelphia, PA: 1817. CMLA. **799**. 51.

—. *Reduction of All the Genera Contained in the Catalogue of North American Plants, to the Natural Families of the French Professor*. See Smith, James Edward. *A Grammar of Botany*.

Necker de Saussure, Jacques. *Plantae Alpinae* (manuscript with nature prints). 1801. HA. **MS19**. 111, *111*.

Nees von Esenbeck, Theodor Friedrich Ludwig. *Plantae Officinales*. Dusseldorf: [1821-]1828-1833. HA. **945**. 110.

Nicander of Colophon. *Les Oeuvres* (with J. Grevin. *Deux Livres de Venins*). Trans. by J. Grevin. Antwerp: 1568-1567. CMLA. **96**. 4.

—. *Theriaca* and *Alexipharmaca*. Venice: 1522-1523. CMLA. **33**. 4.

—. *Theriaca* and *Alexipharmaca*. Trans. by E. Cordus. (With J. Grevin. *De Venenis Libro Duo*. Trans. by H. Martius). Antwerp: 1571. CMLA. **104**. 4.

—. *Theriaca et Alexipharmaca*. Latin translation by J. de Gorrus and Italian translation by A. M. Salvini. Florence: 1764. CMLA. **473**. 4.

Nouveau Traité de la Culture des Jardins Potagers. Paris: 1692. GC. **292**. 114.

Nuttall, Thomas. *The Genera of North American Plants*. Philadelphia, PA: 1818. HA. **813**. 53.

—. *An Introduction to Systematic and Physiological Botany*. Cambridge, MA: 1827. CMLA, HA. **921**. 53, 111.

Orta, Garcia da. *Aromatum, et Simplicium aliquot Medicamentorum apud Indos Nascentium Historia*. Abridged and trans. by C. L'Ecluse. Antwerp: 1574. CMLA. **111**. 15.

—. *Aromatum, et Simplicium aliquot Medicamentorum apud Indos Nascentium Historia*. Abridged and trans. by C. L'Ecluse. Antwerp: 1593. HA. **137**. 15.

Palisot de Beauvois, Ambroise Marie François Joseph. *Compte Verbal ... sur l'Ouvrage de M. de Bridel*. Paris: 1808. HA. **726**.

—. *Flore d'Oware et de Benin*. Paris: 1803. HA. **683**. 52, *52*.

—. *Lettre ... a M. Delamétherie*. Paris: 1814. HA. **775**.

—. *Memoire sur les Lemna*. Paris: 1816. HA. **788**.

—. *Notice sur une Nouvelle Expérience Relative a l'Écorce des Arbres*. Paris: 1811. HA. **753**.

—. *Nouvelles Observations sur la Fructification des Mousses et des Lycopodes*. Paris: 1811. HA. **752**.

—. *Premier [et Second] Mémoire et Observations sur l'Arrangement et la Disposition des Feuilles ...* Paris: 1812. HA. **761**.

Parkinson, John. *Paradisi in Sole Paradisus Terrestris*. London: 1629. CMLA. **179**. 20, *20*.

—. *Theatrum Botanicum*. London: 1640. CMLA, HA. **197**. 20.

Passe, Crispijn van de, the Younger. *Hortus Floridus*. Utrecht and Arnheim: 1614. GC. **160**.65-67, *66*.

—. *Hortus Floridus*. Utrecht and Arnheim: 1616-1617. CMLA. **160**. 65-67, *67*.

Peck, William Dandridge. *A Catalogue of American and Foreign Plants Cultivated in the Botanic Garden.* Cambridge, MA: 1818. HA. **814**. 53-54.

Pena, Pierre, and Matthias de L'Obel. *Nova Stirpium Adversaria.* Antwerp: 1576. CMLA. **115**. 19, 35.

——. *Stirpium Adversaria Nova.* London: 1570-1571. CMLA. **103**. 19, 35, 62, *19*.

Petiver, James. *A Catalogue of Mr. Ray's English Herbal Illustrated with Figures on Folio Copper Plates.* London: 1713. HA. **330**. 40.

The Pharmacopoeia of the United States. Boston, MA: 1820. CMLA. **834**. 29.

Picot de la Peyrouse, Philippe Isadore. *Figures de la Flore des Pyrénées.* Paris: 1795[-1801]. HA. **634**. 86.

Pietro del Toure del Fu Giulio. *Erbario di Numero 400 Piante Fatto per Impressione* (manuscript). Italy: eighteenth century. HA. **MS14**. 73, *74*.

Piso, Willem, and Georg Markgraf. *Historia Naturalis Brasiliae.* Leyden: F. Hack; Amsterdam: 1648. HA. **208**. 16, *17*.

Plantae ad Vivum Depictae (manuscript). CMLA. **MS1**. 73, *73*.

Plinius Secundus, Caius. *The Historie of the World.* Trans. by P. Holland. London: 1601. HA. **148**. 33.

——. *Naturae Historiam Libri XXXVII.* Ed. by J. Kobergius and L. Alantsee. Hagenau: 1518. HA. **30**. 32.

Plumier, Charles. *Plantarum Americanarum.* Ed. by H. Boerhaave. Amsterdam and Leyden: 1755-1760. HA. **440**. 69, 71.

Pol, Nicolaus. *De Cura Morbi Gallici per Lignum Guaycanum, Libellus.* Venice: 1535. CMLA. **47**. 13.

Pomet, Pierre. *A Compleat History of Drugs.* Ed. by J. Hill. London: 1748. CMLA. GC. **328**. 23.

The Pomona Britanica. London: 1788. HA. **582**. 48, 99, *99*.

Porta, Giambattista della. *Phytognomonica.* Frankfurt: J. Wechel and P. Fischer, 1591. HA. **134**. 21, *21*.

Prevost, Jean-Louis. *Collection des Fleurs et des Fruits, Peints d'après Nature.* Paris: [1804-]1806. HA. **701**. 92, *93*.

——. Original painting. HA. **MS21**. 92, *94*.

Pulteney, Richard. *A General View of the Writings of Linnaeus.* London: 1805. GC. **697**. 44.

Pursh, Frederick. *Flora Americae Septentrionalis.* London: 1814. CMLA. **776**. 51.

Rabel, Daniel. *Theatrum Florae.* Paris: 1627. CMLA. **176**. 67, 68.

——. *Theatrum Florae.* Paris: 1633. CMLA, HA. **187**. 67.

Rafinesque, Samuel Constantine. *Caratteri di Alcuni Nuovi Generi e Nuove Specie di Animali e Piante della Sicilia.* Palermo: [1809-]1810. HA.**748**. 53.

——. *Circular Address on Botany and Zoology.* Philadelphia, PA: 1816. HA. **790**. 53.

——. *Medical Flora.* Philadelphia, PA: 1828-1830. CMLA, HA. **946**. 28, *30*.

——. *Principes Fondamentaux de Somiologie.* Palermo: 1814. HA. **777**. 53.

Ray, John. *Catalogus Plantarum Circa Cantabrigiam Nascentium.* Cambridge: 1660. HA. **227**. 40.

——. *De Variis Plantarum Methodis Dissertatio Brevis.* London: 1696. HA. **299**. 41.

——. *Historia Plantarum.* London: 1686-1704. HA. **284**. 40.

——. *Synopsis Methodica Stirpium Britannicarum.* London: 1696. HA. **300**. 41.

Redouté, Pierre Joseph. *Les Liliacées.* Paris: 1802-1816. HA. 677. 88, 88.

——. Original paintings. GC (2, 1822), HA (6, 1813-1816). **MS27, MS26**. 88, *89, 90*.

Redouté, Pierre Joseph, and Claude Antoine Thory. *Les Roses.* Paris: 1817-1824. GC. **807**. 88, 88.

Regnault, Nicolas François. *La Botanique Mise à la Portée de Tout le Monde.* Paris: [1770-]1774[-1780]. HA. **517**. 83, *83*.

Repton, Humphry. *Barton Seagrave in Northamptonshire* (manuscript). 1793-1794. HA. **MS15**. 122, *122*.

——. *Designs for the Pavillon at Brighton*. London: 1808. HA. **728**. 123.

——. *Designs for the Pavillon at Brighton*. undated. GC. **863**. 123.

——. *An Enquiry into the Changes of Taste in Landscape Gardening*. London: 1806. GC, HA. **708**. 123.

——. *Fragments on the Theory and Practice of Landscape Gardening*. London: 1816. HA. **791**. 123.

——. *Observations on the Theory and Practice of Landscape Gardening*. London: 1803. HA. **684**. 123.

——. *Sketches and Hints on Landscape Gardening*. London: 1794. HA. **630**. 122.

Rheede tot Draakestein, Heinrich Adrian van, Johann Casear, Johann Munnicks, and Theodore Janson. *Hortus Malabaricus*. Amsterdam: 1678-1703 (i.e., 1693). HA. **267**. 15, *16*.

Rich, Obadiah. *A Synopsis of the Genera of American Plants*. Georgetown, D.C.: 1814. CMLA. **779**. 54.

Richard, Achille. *Histoire Naturelle et Médicale des Différentes Espèces d'Ipécacuanha du Commerce*. Paris: 1820. CMLA. **836**. 14.

Richard, Louis-Claude Marie. *A Botanical Dictionary*. Trans. by A. Eaton. New Haven, CT: 1817. CMLA. **800**. 55.

Richard, Louis-Claude Marie, and Pierre Bulliard. *A Botanical Grammar and Dictionary*. Trans. by A. Eaton. Albany, NY: 1828. CMLA. **938**. 55.

Richou. *Art de Composer, de Distribuer et de Décorer, a Peu de Frais, Toute Espèce de Jardins*. Paris: 1828 [-1829]. HA. **947**. 119.

Risso, Antoine, and Pierre Antoine Poiteau. *Histoire Naturelle des Orangers*. Paris: 1818. CMLA, HA. **815**. 92.

Rivinus, Augustus Quirinus. *Epistola ad Joan. Raium*. See Ray, John. *Synopsis Methodica Stirpium Britannicarum*.

——. *Introductio Generalis in Rem Herbariam*. Leipzig: 1690. HA. **288**. 41.

——. *Ordo Plantarum, Quae Sunt Flore Irregulari Monopetalo*. Leipzig: 1690. HA. **289**. 41.

——. *Ordo Plantarum, Quae Sunt Flore Irregulari Pentapetalo*. Leipzig: 1699. HA. **308**. 41.

——. *Ordo Plantarum, Quae Sunt Flore Irregulari Tetrapetalo*. Leipzig: 1691. HA. **290**. 41.

Robert, Nicolas. *Fiori Diversi*. Rome: 1640. CMLA. **198**. 68, 68.

——. *Variae ac Multiformes Florum Species Expressae ad Vivum*. Rome: 1665. CMLA. **239**. 68.

Robin, Claude. *Florula Ludoviciana*. Ed. by C. Rafinesque. New York, NY: 1817. HA. **801**. 53.

Robinson, Samuel. *A Course of Fifteen Lectures, on Medical Botany*. Columbus, OH: 1829. CMLA. **965**. 31.

Roques, Joseph. *Phytographie Médicale*. Paris: 1821[-1825]. HA. **855**. 92.

——. *Plantes Usuelles, Indigènes et Exotiques*. Paris: 1807-1808. HA. **720**. 92.

Roscoe, Margaret Lace. *Floral Illustrations of the Seasons*. London: 1829-1831. HA. **969**. 103.

Rose, John. *The English Vineyard Vindicated*. See Bonnefons, Nicolas de. *The French Gardiner*.

Rossi, Giovanni Jacomo. *Giardini di Fiori*. Rome: ca. 1640. CMLA. **201**. 68.

——. *Nova Racolta di Fiori Cavati da Naturale Dati in Luce*. Rome: 1649. CMLA. **209**. 68.

Rousseau, Jean Jacques. *La Botanique* (folio). Paris: 1805. CMLA, HA. **698**. 53, 87.

——. *La Botanique* (quarto). Paris: 1805. HA. **699**. 53, 87.

——. *Letters on the Elements of Botany Addressed to a Lady*. London: 1794. CMLA. **627**. 53.

Rucellai, Giovanni. *Li Api*. See Alamanni, Luigi. *La Coltivazione*.

Ruel, Jean. *De Natura Stirpium Libri Tres*. Paris: 1536. HA. **49**. 33.

Ruiz Lopez, Hipolito. *Quinologia*. Madrid: 1792. HA. **617**. 14

Ruiz Lopez, Hipolito, and José Pavon. *Flora Peruviana et Chilensis*. [Madrid:] 1798-1802[-1807?]. HA. **647**. 80, 84-85, 95-96, *96*.

——. *Florae Peruvianae, et Chilensis, Prodromus*. Madrid: 1794. HA. **629**. 96.

Russell, Alexander. *The Natural History of Aleppo*. London: 1794. CMLA. **628**. 78.

Saint-Hilaire, Auguste de, Adrien Henri Laurent de Jussieu, and Jacques Cambessèdes. *Flora Brasiliae Meridionalis*. Paris: [1824]1825-1832. HA. **906**. 91.

Salerno, School of. *Medicina Salernitana*. Montpellier: 1622. CMLA. **170**. 4.

——. *Medicina Salernitana*. Geneva: 1638. CMLA. **195**. 4.

——. *Regimen Sanitatis*. Trans. by T. Paynel. London: 1541. CMLA. **58**. 4.

——. *Schola Salernitana*. Rotterdam: 1649. CMLA. **210**. 4.

Salisbury, Richard Anthony. *Icones Stirpium Rariorum Descriptionibus Illustratae*. London: 1791. GC. **607**. 100.

Salmon, William. *The Family-Dictionary*. London: 1705. CMLA. **316**. 22.

——. *Botanologia*. London: 1710. CMLA, HA. **325**. 22.

Scheuchzer, Johann Jacob. *Herbarium Diluvianum*. Leyden: 1723. HA. **350**. 55.

Schneevoogt, George Voorhelm. *Icones Plantarum Rariorum*. Harlem: [1792-]1793[-1795]. CMLA, HA. **620**. 97.

Sheldrake, Timothy. *Botanicum Medicinale*. London: [1768?]. HA. **492**. 24.

Sibthorp, John. *Flora Graeca*. London: 1806-1840 [1845 issue]. HA. **713**. 12, 82, 100, *12*, *13*.

——. *Florae Graecae Prodromus*. London: 1806-1813[-1816]. CMLA. **714**. 12.

Silva, Ercola. *Dell'Arte dei Giardini Inglesi*. Milan: ca. 1800. HA. **661**. 123.

Smith, James Edward. *The English Flora*. London: 1824-1828. CMLA, HA. **890**. 48.

——. *A Grammar of Botany Illustrative of Artificial as well as Natural Classification*. New York, NY: 1822. GC. **861**. 54, 111.

——. *Icones Pictae Plantarum Rariorum*. London: 1790-1793. HA. **602**. 100.

——. *An Introduction to Physiological and Systematical Botany*. London: 1809. GC. **736**. 48, 54, 100.

——. *An Introduction to Physiological and Systematical Botany*. Ed. by J. Bigelow. Boston, MA and Philadelphia, PA: 1814. CMLA. **780**. 47, 54.

——. *Syllabus of a Course of Lectures on Botany*. London: 1795. HA **633**. 47.

Société de Botanistes. *Sertum Botanicum*. Brussels: 1828-1832. GC, HA. **950**. 110.

Society of Gardeners. *Catalogus Plantarum*. London: 1730. HA. **370**. 112, *77*.

Sowerby, James. *English Botany*. London: 1790-1814. HA. **601**. 100.

Spaendonck, Gerard van. *Fleurs Dessinées d'après Nature*. Paris; [1801]. HA. **668**. 71-72, *72*.

Spallanzani, Lazzaro. *Dissertations Relative to the Natural History of Animals and Vegetables*. London: 1789. CMLA. **593**. 48.

Speechly, William. *A Treatise on the Culture of the Pineapple*. York: 1779. GC. **537**. 116.

——. *A Treatise on the Culture of the Vine*. York: 1790. GC. **600**. 117.

Spratt, George. *Flora Medica*. London: [1827-]1829-1830. CMLA, HA. **970**. 25, 108, *26*.

Stearns, Samuel. *The American Herbal*. Walpole, NH: 1801, CMLA, GC. **669**. 27.

Steward, William. *Steward's Healing Art*. Saco, ME: 1827. GC. **923**. 29.

Strutt, Jacob George. *Sylva Britannica*. London: 1822[-1826]. HA. **864**. 103, *104*.

Sturm, Jacob, and Johann Wilhelm Sturm. *Deutschlands Flora*. Nuremberg: 1798-1855. HA. **648**. 92.

Sweert, Emanuel. *Florilegium*. Frankfurt: 1612. CMLA. **157**. 65, 112, *64*.

—. *Florilegium*. Arnheim and Frankfurt: 1620-1614. HA. **169**. 65, 112.

—. *Florilegium*. Amsterdam: 1631. CMLA, GC, HA. **182**. 65, 112.

—. *Florilegium*. Amsterdam: 1641. CMLA. **202**. 65, 112.

—. *Florilegium*. Amsterdam: 1647. CMLA, HA. **207**. 65, 112.

Sweet, Robert. *The British Flower Garden*. London: 1823-1829. HA. **872**. 101.

—. *Flora Australasica*. London: 1827-1828. HA. **929**. 101.

—. *The Florist's Guide, and Cultivator's Directory*. London: 1827-1832. HA. **930**. 102.

—. *Geraniaceae*. London: 1820-1830. HA. **840**. 101.

Tabernaemontanus, Jacobus Theodorus. *Eicones Plantarum*. Frankfurt: 1590. HA. **133**. 62.

—. *Neuw Kreuterbuch*. Frankfurt: 1587-1588; 1591. CMLA. **130**. 62.

Ten Lithographic Coloured Flowers with Botanical Descriptions. Edinburgh: 1826. HA. **911**. 108.

Thacher, James. *The American New Dispensatory*. Boston, MA: 1810. CMLA. **743**. 27.

—. *The American Orchardist*. Boston, MA: 1822. GC. **861A**. 116.

Theophrastus of Eresos. *De Historia et Causis Plantarum Libri Quindecim*. Trans. by T. Gaza. Paris: 1529.
HA. **39**. 32.

—. *De Historia Plantarum Libri Decem*. Ed. by J. Badaeus à Stapel with the translation of
T. Gaza. Amsterdam: 1644. CMLA, HA. **204**. 32.

—. *Dell'Historia delle Piante*. Trans. by M. A. Biondo. Venice: 1549. HA. **70**. 32.

Thomson, Samuel. *A Narrative of the Life and Medical Discoveries of Samuel Thomson*. Boston, MA: 1822.
CMLA. **862**. 30-31.

—. *A Narrative of the Life and Medical Discoveries of Samuel Thomson* and *New Guide to Health*.
Boston, MA: 1825. CMLA. **902**. 30-31.

—. *A Narrative of the Life and Medical Discoveries of Samuel Thomson*. Columbus, OH: 1827.
CMLA. **924**. 30-31.

—. *A Narrative of the Life and Medical Discoveries of Samuel Thomson*. St. Clairsville, OH: 1829.
CMLA. **966**. 30-31.

Thorburn, Grant. *The Gentleman and Gardener's Kalendar*. New York, NY: 1821. GC. **845**. 116.

Thornton, Robert John. *Botanical Extracts, or, Philosophy of Botany*. London: 1810. HA. **744**. 106.

—. *The British Flora*. London: 1812. CMLA. **762**. 80, 107.

—. *A New Family Herbal*. London: 1810. GC, HA. **745**. 26, 27.

—. *New Illustrations of the Sexual System of Carolus von Linnaeus*. London: [1798-]1807-
[1810]. CMLA, HA. **722**. 103-107, *104-106*.

—. *Temple of Flora*. [London:] 1812. GC. **763**. 107, *105*.

Thouin, Gabriel. *Plans Raisonnés de Toutes les Espèces de Jardins*. Paris: 1820. HA. **838**. 119.

Thunberg, Carl Peter. *Flora Japonica*. Leipzig: 1784. GC, HA. **554**. 47, *47*.

Tissot, Samuel Auguste Andre David. *Advice to the People in General with Regard to Their Health*. London:
1765. CMLA. **478**. 22.

—. *Avis au Peuple sur Sa Santé*. Paris: 1765; 1764. CMLA. **477**. 22.

Torrey, John. *A Compendium of the Flora of the Northern and Middle States of the United States*. New York,
NY: 1826. CMLA. **913**. 55.

Tournefort, Joseph Pitton de. *Elemens de Botanique*. Paris: 1694. CMLA, GC, HA. **296**. 69, *71*.

Tosa, Mitsunari. Original paintings. HA. **MS7**. 69, *71*.

Trew, Christoph Jakob. *Hortus Nitidissimis Omnem per Annum Superbiens Floribus*. Nuremberg:
[1750-]1768-1786[-1792]. HA. **493**. 78, *78*.

Trew, Christoph Jakob, and Benedict Christian Vogel. *Plantae Selectae*. Augsburg: 1750-1773. HA. **429**. 78.

Turner, William. *The Herbal*. Cologne: 1568. CMLA, HA. **99**. 18, *18*.

Tussac, François Richard. *Flore des Antilles*. Paris: 1808-1827[1828]. HA. **733**. 91.

Vaillant, Sebastien. *Botanicon Parisiense*. Ed. by H. Boerhaave. Leyden and Amsterdam: 1727. HA. **360**. 69.

Vallet, Pierre. *Le Jardin du Roy Tres Chrestien Henry IV*. [Paris]: 1608. CMLA. **154**. 62, *63*.

Vandelli, Domenico. *Diccionario dos Termos Technicos de Historia Natural*. Coimbra: 1788. HA. **583**. 49.

Van Huysum, School of. Original paintings. HA. **MS5**. 96-97.

Velloso, José Mariano Conceiçao. *Florae Flumensis Icones*. Paris: 1827[-1832]. HA. **931**. 110.

Ventenat, Etienne Pierre. *Choix de Plantes dont la Plupart Sont Cultivées dans le Jardin de Cels*. Paris: 1803[-1808]. HA. **688**. 88.

Versailles Illustrated. London: ca. 1740. GC. **394**. 119, *120*.

Vienna Porzellan-Manufaktur Group. Original paintings. HA. **MS18**. 80, *82*.

Vigneux, A. *Flore Pittoresque des Environs de Paris*. Paris: 1812. HA. **764**. 92.

Vincent of Beauvais. *Speculum Doctrinale*. Strassburg: c. 1477. CMLA. **A1**. 33.

Vues et Descriptions du Jardin des Plantes. Paris: 1813. HA. **769**. 119.

Wagner, Daniel. *Pharmaceutisch-Medicinisch Botanik*. Vienna: 1828-1829[-1830]. HA. **951**. 110.

Walker, John M. *An Experimental Inquiry into the Similarity in Virtue between the Cornus Florida and Sericea, and the Cinchona Officinalis of Linnaeus*. Philadelphia, PA: 1803. HA. **685**. 14.

Walpole, Horace. *Essay on Modern Gardening*. See Marshall, William. *On Planting and Rural Ornament*.

Waterhouse, Benjamin. *The Botanist* and *The Principle of Vitality*. Boston, MA: 1811. CMLA. **755**. 51.

Watkins, Thomas. *The Art of Promoting the Growth of the Cucumber and Melon*. London: 1824. GC. **886**. 116.

Wedel, Georg Wolffgang. *Opiologia*. Jena: 1682. CMLA. **A2**. 14.

Weinmann, Johann Wilhelm. *Phytanthoza-Iconographia*. Regensburg: 1737-1745. HA. **388**. 76, *76*.

——. *Phytanthoza-Iconographia*. Augsburg: 1745. HA. **405**. 76.

——. *Weinmannus Redivivus Emendatus et Illustratus, sive Thesaurus Rei Herbariae Locupletissimus*. Augsburg: [1737-]1787. HA. **575**. 76.

Whitlaw, Charles. *Whitlaw's New Medical Discoveries with a Defence of the Linnaean Doctrine*. London: 1829. CMLA. **967**. 26.

Withering, William. *An Account of the Foxglove*. Birmingham: 1785. CMLA. **562**. 14, *14*.

——. *A Botanical Arrangement of All the Vegetables Naturally Growing in Great Britain*. Birmingham: 1776. CMLA. **527**. 48.

Woodville, William. *Medical Botany*. London: 1790-1794[-1795]. HA. **603**. 25, 100, *25*.

Stanley H. Johnston is a native of Cleveland, Ohio. He received his undergraduate degree in English from Columbia University and his M.A. and Ph.D. from the University of Western Ontario where his studies centered on Bibliography and Medieval and Renaissance literature. His bio-bibliographical dissertation was on the books and career of Richard Pynson, King's Printer to Henry VII and Henry VIII. He later received his library degree from Case Western Reserve University where he also studied archives. He is currently Curator of Rare Books at the Holden Arboretum where he offers classes in the history of the book and various aspects of the Warren H. Corning Collection of Horticultural Classics. He is active in the Council on Botanical and Horticultural Libraries for which he writes a column on botanical and horticultural web sites. He is the author of *The Cleveland Herbal, Botanical and Horticultural Collections* (1992) which provides detailed bibliographical descriptions of the books discussed in this volume.